# advanced BASIC

# Hayden Computer Programming Series

# advanced BASIC

## APPLICATIONS AND PROBLEMS

### JAMES S. COAN

*Community Computer Corporation*
*Germantown Friends School*

# HAYDEN BOOK COMPANY, INC.
Rochelle Park, New Jersey

Library of Congress Cataloging in Publication Data

Coan, James S
    Advanced BASIC.

   (Hayden computer programming series)
   Bibliography: p.
   Includes index.
   1. Basic (Computer program language).
2. Mathematics--Data processing. I. Title.
QA76.73.B3C6      001.6'425     76-7435
ISBN 0-8104-5856-X
ISBN 0-8104-5855-1 pbk.

| 8 | 9 | PRINTING |
|---|---|---|

| 79 | 80 | 81 | 82 | 83 | 84 | 85 | YEAR |
|----|----|----|----|----|----|----|------|

# PREFACE

Students are finding that after they have been through the introductory texts presenting BASIC they are pretty much on their own. They may get additional bits and pieces of assistance from other texts, finding that each adds something to their repertoire, but there is still all that introductory material to sort through. The present text is intended for those who have been introduced to the BASIC language and want to go further with the language. It is also intended for those who have already learned another language (such as FORTRAN or COBOL) and need only a brief introduction to what is for them a second or third programming language.

A review chapter is placed at the beginning of the book for those whose coverage of BASIC may have been somewhat limited or distant in time, and for those who come to it with competence in one or more other programming languages. In fact, this text can even be used by students with no former programming experience, if tutorial assistance is available, by a more extensive use of the review chapter.

Some extended features of BASIC are presented so that students working on systems providing extensions will have an opportunity to experiment with or master new techniques. Strings and files are introduced in Chapters 3 and 4. Due to the variety of implementations for use of both strings and files, two systems are presented in each area: General Electric and Hewlett Packard.

In addition to other topics, the applications chapters cover coordinate geometry, area, sequences and series, polynomials, graphing, simulation, and games. These chapters may be studied independently and in any order, although, where appropriate, the student may occasionally be referred to another section in the text. Generally these topics evolve from or build on the ground of a second course in algebra and beyond.

The topic of efficiency is treated explicitly on several occasions, though not necessarily to the point of optimizing execution time. The topic of structured programming is treated implicitly in that all example programs incorporate a clear programming style with minimal unconditional branching and maximal use of appropriate data and control structures. These two topics provide good stepping-off points in a computer science course.

Appendix A presents an abbreviation of the ASCII character codes. Appendices B and C summarize flowchart shapes and program statements in BASIC. Appendix D is an index of the nearly 100 demonstration programs in the text. Some solution programs for selected problems in the text follow these appendices.

I wish to thank Community Computer Corporation for computer time, General Electric Information Services for assistance, and those who commented on the first draft for invaluable suggestions.

JAMES S. COAN

*Philadelphia*

# CONTENTS

# 1
# REVIEW OF
# BASIC

## 1-1  Introduction

This chapter is intended to serve several purposes. The student who is already competent in BASIC will move quickly through the chapter and perhaps write a few programs. The student who has studied BASIC, but not recently or not extensively, will want to move more slowly and write more programs. The student who comes to BASIC with competence in another language will be mainly interested in the differences between the language with which he or she is familiar and BASIC.

There are numerous implementations of BASIC available in schools, colleges, and businesses today. These implementations have many common features and some differences. This chapter will concentrate primarily on those features which are almost universally available. We will mention some of the more common variations (you can usually determine which features are part of your system by writing very short programs to see what works), but beyond that the student should obtain the specific features for his system from the BASIC reference manuals supplied by the computer center or the vendor.

It is also true that the specifications sometimes change as the people responsible for maintaining the computer update its language capabilities. Since these changes tend to be additions, however, programs previously tested will usually still run.

## 1-2  Some Simple Programs

We can demonstrate many features of BASIC by writing a program that will compare two numbers to determine whether the first is greater than, less than, or equal to the second. See program CØMPAR.

```
LIST
COMPAR

94      REM * THIS IS A SAMPLE PROGRAM TO
95      REM  COMPARE TWO NUMBERS FOR ORDER
100     READ A,B
110       IF A = .01 THEN 220
120       IF A = B THEN 160
130       IF A < B THEN 180
140     PRINT A; "IS GREATER THAN"; B
150     GOTO 100
160     PRINT A; "IS EQUAL TO"; B
170     GOTO 100
180     PRINT A; "IS LESS THAN"; B
190     GOTO 100
192
194     REM
200     DATA   3,4,   1.7,1.1,   31,31,   -3,2,   0,0
210     DATA   .01,0
220     END
RUN
COMPAR

 3 IS LESS THAN 4
 1.7 IS GREATER THAN 1.1
 31 IS EQUAL TO 31
-3 IS LESS THAN 2
 0 IS EQUAL TO 0
```

The first item shown is LIST. This is a system command rather than a program statement, and we type it to instruct the computer to print out the program exactly as it stands. Next the computer automatically prints CØMPAR, which is the program name. Some computers also print the time of day and date along with the program name. On some systems we assign program names with the system command NAME-CØMPAR. On others, to name a new program, NEW CØMPAR is typed before the program itself is. Having typed the program name, the computer goes on to list the program itself. Let us examine the program statements.

## Read-Data

Line 100 is a READ statement. In this case we want the computer to READ two numbers into two variables A and B. Those numbers must come from one or more DATA statements. We provide data in lines 200 and 210.

## Conditional Transfer

Lines 110, 120, and 130 are all examples of the conditional transfer in BASIC. Line 110 is used to terminate the execution of the program itself. We send the computer to the END statement only if the value of A is .01. This is an example of the use of dummy data to control program execution. Lines 120 and 130 direct the computer to the appropriate PRINT statement according to the relation between the values of A and B. BASIC also allows "greater than" ($>$), "greater than or equal to" ($>=$) and "less than or equal to" ($<=$). To test for "not equal to" use ($<>$). Some systems also allow "#" for "not equal to."

In place of the algebraic symbols just mentioned, some systems require special symbols as relational operators. They are (\LT) or (LT) for "less than,"

(\LE) or (LE) for "less than or equal to," (\GT) or (GT) for "greater than," (\GE) or (GE) for "greater than or equal to," (\EQ) or (EQ) for "equal to" and (\NE) or (NE) for "not equal to." The paired relational operators listed above are not generally interchangable. The first is for certain systems, and the second is for others. So there are three sets of possible relational operators. You can quickly tell which works on your computer by consulting the vendor-supplied manual or by trial and error.

Another conditional transfer is available on many systems. It is called the computed G$\emptyset$T$\emptyset$. It takes the form,

$$100 \quad \emptyset N \ K \ G\emptyset T\emptyset \ n_1,n_2,n_3, \text{etc.}$$

or

$$100 \quad G\emptyset T\emptyset \ K \ \emptyset F \ n_1,n_2,n_3, \text{etc.}$$

or

$$100 \quad G\emptyset T\emptyset \ n_1,n_2,n_3, \text{etc}, \emptyset N \ K$$

At line 100 computer control passes to line $n_1$ if K = 1, $1_2$ if K = 2, etc. If K is not in the range from one to the number of line numbers named, some systems terminate with an error message, while others simply pass control to the line after 100.

## Print

Lines 140, 160, and 180 result in printed output to the terminal for the operator to see. We may mix literal output with numeric results by enclosing literal messages in quotation marks. Replacing semicolons in the PRINT statement with commas would result in wider spacing of printed output. On many systems, using commas to separate printed results causes the page to be divided into five columns of 15 characters each. For terminals with only 72 character spaces, the fifth column is 12 characters wide. Generally speaking, use of a semicolon to separate printed output results in closer spacing than with a comma.

## Unconditional Transfer

Lines 150, 170, and 190 are examples of unconditional transfer. The G$\emptyset$T$\emptyset$ statement in BASIC serves to name the number of the next line to be executed. When the computer gets to line 150, the next line the computer executes is 100. The same is true for lines 170 and 190. Generally speaking, good programs try to minimize the number of G$\emptyset$T$\emptyset$ statements. We shall see ways to do this later.

## End

The final statement in our example is the END statement. On most systems the highest numbered statement must be an END statement. After the END statement we see the system command RUN, which is typed by us to cause the computer to actually carry out the instructions of the program. In response to the RUN command, the computer has printed the program name, C$\emptyset$MPAR (some systems will also print the date and time), followed by the printed output specified by the instructions of our program. (Some systems will follow program results with information about the computer resources used by this RUN of the program.)

## Variables

In program CØMPAR we used A and B as variables to name stored numeric values. BASIC allows us to use every letter of the alphabet and also every letter of the alphabet followed by a single digit. (Some systems also provide additional symbols as variables.) Every letter or letter plus digit allows us to store a single number at any one time in a program. However, variables may be used over and over again to store new values as long as we have no further need for a particular old value. In CØMPAR, the variables A and B were each used for six different numbers.

## Prettyprinting

Note the overall appearance of program CØMPAR. An attempt has been made to provide spacing within the program statements to facilitate readability and therefore clarity of thought. The practice of indenting and spacing to achieve this goal is called "prettyprinting." In program CØMPAR, the IF statements have been indented three spaces. Spaces have been inserted in the PRINT statements to avoid a crowded appearance. The blank REM in line 194 is used to offset the DATA portion of the program, and the data has been grouped in the DATA statements to show just how the values will be read in the READ statement. Some systems do not allow prettyprinting. However, if your system does allow prettyprinting, you should work on developing a style of spacing to enhance program readability. Prettyprinting becomes more and more worthwhile as programs become longer and more complex.

## Arithmetic Operations

The computer is often used to perform arithmetic operations on numbers. The operations allowed are exponentiation (**) or (↑), multiplication (*), division (/), addition (+) and subtraction (-). The priorities assigned these operators are the same as those assigned in conventional algebra, that is, first exponentiation followed by multiplication and division followed by addition and subtraction. Program ØPRATN shows a use of each of the arithmetic operators.

```
CPRATN

94   REM * THIS IS A SAMPLE PROGRAM TO DEMONSTRATE
95   REM USE CF ARITHMETIC OPERATORS IN BASIC
100  PRINT   "A↑B", "A*B", "A/B", "A+B", "A-B"
110  READ A,B
120     IF A <> 0 THEN 150
130     IF B <> 0 THEN 150
140  STOP
150  PRINT "        A =";  A;  "B =";  B
160  PRINT   A↑B,  A*B,  A/B,  A+B,  A-B
170  PRINT
180  GOTO  110
182
184  REM
190  DATA  1,2,   3,4,   2,40,   1.4,65.2
200  DATA  0,0
210  END
```

```
RUN
OPRATN

A↑B                 A*B         A/B          A+B         A-B
        A = 1  B = 2
   1                 2          0.5           3           -1

        A = 3  B = 4
  81                12          0.75          7           -1

        A = 2  B = 40
1.09951E+12         80          0.05          42          -38

        A = 1.4  B = 65.2
3.36936E+9         91.28        2.14724E-2    66.6        -63.8
```

The RUN of ∅PRATN produces three examples of what is called E-format. For A = 2 and B = 40, A**B results in 1.09951E+12. That means 1.09951 times 10 to the twelfth power, or $1.09951 \times 10^{12}$. Systems vary, but many provide from six to nine significant digits of numeric output.

In ∅PRATN, line 140 is equivalent to G∅T∅ 210. The ST∅P statement in BASIC is used to terminate execution of a program at some point other than the highest numbered line. This line of the program is called a "logical end" to differentiate it from the physical end.

## Assignment

Thus far, the way that we have gotten numeric values to be stored in variables has been to READ values from DATA. We can also assign values directly as follows:

|   |          |    |     |            |
|---|----------|----|-----|------------|
| 100 | X = 3    | or | 100 | LET X = 3  |
| 200 | Y = 3*X+5 | or | 200 | LET T = 3*X+5 |

These are examples of the assignment statement in BASIC. (On some systems the LET is required. On others it is optional.) Used in this way, the equals sign is called the assignment operator. The assignment capability greatly enhances the power of any programming language since it permits us to retain values for later use. For example, we can sum up any number of data items as in program ADD.

```
ADD

    94    REM * THIS PROGRAM ADDS NUMBERS FROM DATA
 →  100   LET S = 0
    110   READ A
    120      IF A = -.01 THEN 160
    140   LET S = S+A
    150   GOTO 110
    160   PRINT  "SUM IS"; S
    172
    174   REM
    180   DATA   21, 39, 11.3, 24.6, 91.3
    190   DATA   -.01
    200   END
RUN
ADD

SUM IS 187.2
```

In line 100 of ADD the summing variable S is initialized at zero. (Some implementations of BASIC automatically initialize all variables to zero when the program is run.) We now generalize program ADD to count the number of numbers in the previous program. See lines 100, 130, and 140 of ADD1.

```
ADD1

94    REM * THIS PROGRAM ADDS AND COUNTS
95    REM  NUMBERS FROM DATA
→100  LET S = C = 0
110   READ A
120     IF A = -.01 THEN 160
→130  LET C = C+1
→140  LET S = S+A
150   GOTO 110
160   PRINT  "SUM IS"; S
170   PRINT  "THERE ARE"; C; "NUMBERS"
172
174   REM
180   DATA   21, 39, 11.3, 24.6, 91.3
190   DATA  -.01
200   END
RUN
ADD1

SUM IS 187.2
THERE ARE 5 NUMBERS
```

Line 100 of ADD1 is an example of a multiple assignment statement. It allows us to assign the rightmost value to all of the variables separated by equals signs. (Some systems require commas instead of equals signs for all but the rightmost equals signs. Our statement 100 would be 100  LET S,C = 0 on such a system. You may be able to assign different values to different variables on one line, for example, 100  LET H = 4, Y = 9*K, B = 81, or even 100  LET H,I,J = 3, T = -32.)

## Input

The final statement of this review section which results in variables containing numeric values is the INPUT statement. It is this statement which allows the operator to interact with a program during execution. When the computer executes an input statement, it prints a question mark at the terminal and awaits information from the keyboard. If we replace READ A with INPUT A in program ADD and remove the DATA statement, we have a program that behaves a little like an adding machine. By printing a marker such as # followed by a semicolon in line 130 we can type our selected numbers on the same line as the marker, as in program ADD2.

```
ADD2

94    REM * THIS PROGRAM WORKS A LITTLE
95    REM  LIKE AN ADDING MACHINE
100   PRINT  "INPUT # = -.01 TO OBTAIN TOTAL"
110   PRINT
120   LET S = 0
→130  PRINT  "#";
140   INPUT A
150     IF A = -.01 THEN 180
160   LET S = S+A
```

```
170   GOTO 130
180   PRINT   "SUM IS"; S
190   END
RUN
ADD2

INPUT # = -.01 TO OBTAIN TOTAL

#? 45
#? 78
#? 34
#? 98.12
#? 43
#? -.01
SUM IS 298.12
```

Note that input statements may be used to call for several values. 100 IN-PUT X,Y,B9 calls for three numbers to be typed, separated by commas at the keyboard.

## Summary of Sec. 1-2

We have looked at three system commands to give a program a name, in-struct the computer to RUN a program, and to LIST a program. We have used the following eight statements in programs; READ, DATA, IF-THEN, PRINT, END, STØP, LET, and INPUT. With just these statements we are able to write substantial programs (nevertheless, the language does contain tremendous ad-ditional power in other statements to come in the next sections). The concepts of variable and program control have been discussed. We have looked at three kinds of operators: arithmetic, relational, and assignment.

## Problems for Sec. 1-2

1) Write a program to average numbers entered as DATA or on INPUT.
2) Write a program to find the largest and/or smallest number of a set of DATA.
3) Write a program to repeatedly average groups of numbers.
4) Write a program to add all positive integers from 1 to n, where n is an item of DATA.
5) Write a program to calculate n factorial. Be sure to make the value of 0! equal 1.
6) Write a program to solve equations of the form, $ax + b = cx + d$.
7) Write a program to solve quadratic equations, $ax^2 + bx + c = 0$.
8) Write a program to find the sum of the reciprocals of the first n positive integers.

## 1-3  Functions, Loops and Lists

BASIC provides computer functions or subroutines for special purposes. INT(X), SGN(X), ABS(X), and SQR(X) are among them. On some systems the INT(X) function takes the greatest integer not greater than X, such as 4 for 4.3 and $-2$ for $-1.6$. Other systems simply give the integral part of X, such as 4 for 4.3 and $-1$ for $-1.6$, by removing the decimal part. For non-negative numbers, the two are equivalent. SGN(X) becomes $+1$ if X is positive, zero if X is zero, and $-1$ if X is negative. ABS(X) becomes X if X is non-negative and becomes $-X$ if X is negative. SQR(X) becomes the principle square root of X so long as X is non-negative. Each of these functions is useful. However, it is likely that of the four, INT(X) is most frequently used.

One use of INT(X) is to round off numeric results. For example, to round to the nearest integer, use INT(X+.5). To round to the nearest hundredth, use INT(100*X+.5)/100, etc. See line 150 of program RØUND.

```
ROUND

94    REM * THIS PROGRAM DEMONSTRATES A USE OF THE
95    REM   INT( ) FUNCTION IN BASIC FOR ROUNDING
96    REM   NUMBERS
100   LET E = 0
110   LET X = 1.82564
120   PRINT  "ROUND"; X
130   PRINT
140   PRINT  "POWER OF TENTHS", " ROUNDS TO"
→150  LET R = INT( X*10↑E+.5 )/10↑E
160   PRINT  E, R
162
164   REM * LINE 170 INCREMENTS THE EXPONENT OF 10
170   LET E = E+1
180      IF E <= 5 THEN 150
190   END
RUN
ROUND

ROUND 1.82564

POWER OF TENTHS ROUNDS TO
0                2
1                1.8
2                1.83
3                1.826
4                1.8256
5                1.82564
```

INT(X) is also used frequently to test numbers for divisibility by other numbers. For example:

$$100 \quad \text{IF } X/10 = \text{INT}(X/10) \text{ THEN } 200$$

transfers the computer to line 200 if X is divisible by 10, but the computer goes to the line immediately following 100 if X is not divisible by 10. One problem solution that uses this is that of finding all factors of a certain number. We simply try all integers from 2 to the number and test for divisibility. If the divisor goes evenly, we print it; if not, we go to the next divisor. This is left as an exercise.

## Random Numbers

BASIC provides a routine to generate pseudo-random numbers. These are very useful as a source of data for simulating random events. The procedure varies somewhat from system to system. All systems provide decimal numbers in the range, 0 to 1. One procedure introduces random numbers by using RND(X) in a statement such as 100 LET A = RND(X). The particular random numbers are duplicated or different from one run to the next according to the value of X. If X is negative, then you get a different set of random numbers from run to run. If X is 0, then each run of the program produces the same succession of random numbers. And if X is positive, then the set of random numbers is based on the value of X. A second procedure does not require an argument for RND. The statement 100 LET A = RND selects a random number and assigns it to A. However, used alone it generates the same set of random numbers from one run to the next. To obtain a different set of random numbers from run to run, simply introduce the companion statement 10 RANDØ-MIZE into the program. The ability to reproduce the same set of random numbers is useful for finding errors in the program debugging process. Once the program has been perfected, it can then be modified to produce different results for each run.

Most of the uses for random numbers are for numbers in some range other than 0 to 1. So we have to do the appropriate calculations to change the range. For example, to "roll a die" we would use 100 LET R = INT(6*RND(-1)+1) or 100 LET R = INT(6*RND+1). This would give integers in the range 1 to 6 inclusive. In the statement, 200 LET N = INT(A*RND+B), A specifies the possible number of random integers and B specifies the smallest possible random integer.

## Loops

Suppose we place ten slips of paper numbered 1 to 10 into a hat and have five people draw one slip of paper, note the number on it, and return the slip to the hat. This we can easily do with a program, as in program DRAW.

Program DRAW and several other programs we have looked at contain examples of repetitive steps. This is a computer loop, and BASIC provides the FØR-NEXT statement pair to set up loops. Program DRAW01 uses FØR-NEXT to accomplish the same purpose as program DRAW. Note that both programs simulate returning the slips to the hat.

```
DRAW

94    REM * THIS PRØGRAM SIMULATES RANDCM DRAWING
95    REM  FIVE NUMBERS FROM AMØNG 10 WITH REPLACEMENT
100   RANDØMIZE
110   LET X = 1
120   LET R = INT( RND*10+1 )
130   PRINT R;
140   LET X = X+1
150      IF X <= 5 THEN 120
160   END
RUN
DRAW

 6   9   6   10   8


DRAW01

94    REM * THIS PRØGRAM DIFFERS FRØM DRAW
95    REM  IN THAT FOR-NEXT IS NCW INTRCDUCED
100   RANDØMIZE
110   FØR X = 1 TO 5
120      LET R = INT( RND*10+1 )
130      PRINT R;
140   NEXT X
142
150   END
RUN
DRAW01

 2   9   5   2   10
```

*Lists*

Now suppose that the five people who drew slips of paper from the hat did not replace them. We must make sure that no number is drawn twice. In order to achieve this goal we need to be able to keep track of what numbers have been drawn and what numbers are left. This can be done rather nicely using a subscripted variable called a "list." A list, designated by a single letter, reserves space for more than one number. At the time that we first designate a list variable, the computer automatically reserves 10 locations (some computers reserve 11 by allowing zero as a subscript). We can simulate the numbered slips of paper in the hat by establishing a 10-item list with the integers 1 through 10 stored in locations 1 through 10. This is done by the following routine:

```
100   FOR I = 1 TO 10
110      LET L(I) = I
120   NEXT I
```

Line 110 sets up the subscripted variable L( ) so that $L(1) = 1, L(2) = 2$, etc., through $L(10) = 10$. If we need more than 10, we can get them by using the DIMension statement. This is usually placed at the very beginning of the program. For example, if we want 25 slips of paper in our hat, we would begin with 10 DIM L(25), and 25 locations would be available. Note that we could dimension for 25 and then use only 10 of them, but we cannot use more than the DIM statement specifies. Any number of lists may be dimensioned on the same line as: 10 DIM A(36), B(43). Systems allow a maximum number of storage locations from a few thousand to many thousands.

Now we can develop a procedure to select five numbers at random without replacement. For the first draw there will be 10 numbers from which to draw; for the second draw one has been removed, leaving nine. The process is repeated until there remain only six from which to draw for the last draw. This can be done with another FØR-NEXT pair. We can step backwards with FØR J = 10 TØ 6 STEP -1. We may specify all three numbers on the right of the equals sign by variable or formula.

If we design a program that merely checks to see if the latest number has already been drawn, then we get into a trial and error situation. And if we try to draw 10 numbers from among 10, or worse yet, 100 from 100, the drawing gets slower and slower as we get nearer and nearer to the last draw (adding suspense and expense). For efficiency's sake we should avoid this pure trial and error scheme. Thus consider the following procedure for eliminating trial and error entirely.

For the first draw we may select a number R at random from one to 10. We may use the value of L(R) as the number on our randomly selected slip of paper. If we draw the same value of R later on, we need a method that does not require testing to see if L(R) has been used. We can acheive this by simply replacing the value of L(R) with the value of L(J) where J is the number of slips from which the drawing is being made after each drawn number has been printed. The important consideration here is that this scheme allows us to use every number that is drawn. We have taken care here to develop an efficient algorithm to solve the problem submitted to us. See in particular line 160 in program DRAW02.

```
DRAW02

94    REM * THIS PROGRAM SIMULATES RANDOM DRAWING WITHOUT
95    REM  REPLACEMENT AND WITHOUT TRIAL AND ERROR
96
97    REM * LINES 100-120 SIMULATE 10 SLIPS
98    REM  OF PAPER IN A HAT
99    RANDOMIZE
100   FOR I = 1 TO 10
110      LET L(I) = I
120   NEXT I
122
124   REM * NOW DRAW FIVE NUMBERS AT RANDOM
130   FOR J = 10 TO 6 STEP -1
140      LET R = INT( RND*J+1 )
150      PRINT L(R);
152
154      REM * NOW REPLACE THE NUMBER JUST PRINTED
155      REM  WITH THE LAST NUMBER IN THE LIST
160      LET L(R) = L(J)
170   NEXT J
172
180   END
RUN
DRAW02

 9  7  3  4  5
```

We can see from a run of DRAW02 that no number has been drawn more than once, but one run is not a certainty. A further check can be made by drawing all 10. We leave this as an exercise.

## More Functions

In addition to the functions already described, the following are universally available: SIN, CØS, ATN, LØG, and EXP. SIN(X), CØS(X) and TAN(X) give the sine, cosine, and tangent of X, where X is taken as an abstract dimensionless number or the measure of an angle in radians. ATN(X) gives the principle arctangent in radians, where X is the tangent of the required number. LØG(X) gives the natural logarithm of a non-negative X and EXP(X) gives $e^X$. Besides these there are other functions which may or may not be available on a particular system. Among these will be log base 10, secant, cosecant, etc. On some systems CLK(X) gives the present time using a 24-hour clock, and TIM(X) gives the elapsed time of program run in seconds. It is best to consult the manual for your system to determine the full extent of function capabilities.

## Summary of Sec. 1-3

BASIC generally provides INT, SQR, SGN, ABS, SIN, CØS, TAN, ATN, EXP, and LØG as standard functions, where trigonometric functions are based on radian measure and exponentials use e as the base. The routine RND is available to provide random numbers. The language created loop is FØR A = B TØ C STEP D, where the loop variable A first takes on the value of B and increments by D until A passes C and control passes to the next line following NEXT A which closes the BASIC loop. The default STEP value is always 1. The list is available as a subscripted variable to allow block storage of several numbers attached to a single letter. The DIM statement is required for subscripts exceeding 10.

## Problems for Sec. 1-3

1) Write a program to find the absolute value without using any of the functions introduced in this section.
2) Write a program to find the greatest integer in X without using the INT function. Be certain it works for negative numbers.
3) Write a program to roll two dice.
4) Write an efficient program to deal four 13 card hands from a standard 52 card bridge deck.
5) Write a program to store 25 random numbers in a list, print them all, and print the largest and the smallest along with their respective positions in the list.
6) Write a program to print all factors of an integer entered on INPUT.
7) Write a program to print prime integers in the range 2001 to 2501.
8) Find the greatest common factor for pairs of integers.
9) Find the least common multiple for pairs of integers.
10) Generate 100 integers at random from one to 10. Use a list to tabulate their frequency of occurrence.
11) Write a program to print a table of trigonometric values in a 10 degree range by intervals of 20 minutes. Pick any one function.
12) Modify DRAW02 to draw all 10 slips of paper.
13) Write a program to produce the results of CØMPAR using SGN(A − B) and the computed GØTØ statement.

## 1-4  User Defined Functions, Subroutines, and Arrays

*User Defined Functions*

Another kind of computer function is available in BASIC. It is called the "user defined function" and has the following form:

$$100 \quad DEF\ FNA(X) = [formula]$$

If the A is positioned in FNA(X), you may use instead any letter of the alphabet as the identifier, thus designating up to 26 functions in any one program. For example, we might want to round off results to the nearest hundredth in several places in a program. We would then use

$$100 \quad DEF\ FNH(X) = INT(X*100+.5)/100$$

and then use FNH( ), placing whatever variable we want rounded off in the parentheses. Generally speaking, programmers place DEF statements near the beginning of the program, and some systems require that this be done. Some systems allow only a single argument; some allow two or more; some allow none. We may use any variable or legal BASIC expression, including a defined function, as an argument.

Suppose we define a polynomial function, select a few values of X between −10 and 10 at random and round the results to the nearest tenth. See program PRT.

Defined functions are useful whenever we wish the computer to return a single value.

```
PRT

94    REM * THIS PROGRAM DEMONSTRATES THE SINGLE
95    REM  LINE DEFINED FUNCTION IN BASIC
99    RANDOMIZE
→100   DEF FNP(K) = 3.41*K↑3 + 4.32*K↑2 - 11.2*K + 16.73
→110   DEF FNR(K) = INT( K*RND+1 )
→120   DEF FNT(K) = INT( K*10+.5 )/10
130   PRINT  "X", "FNP(X)", "FNT(FNP(X))"
140   FOR C = 1 TO 5
150     LET X = FNR(21)-11
160      PRINT  X, FNP(X), FNT(FNP(X))
170   NEXT C
172
180   END
RUN
PRT

X                FNP(X)           FNT(FNP(X))
 8               1949.53           1949.5
 6                841.61            841.6
-5               -245.52           -245.5
10               3746.73           3746.7
-8              -1363.11          -1363.1
```

## Subroutines

If we want the computer to return with two or more values, we cannot use a defined function. Also, in the unlikely case that we want more than 26 functions, we need a new capability. In such cases we use a subroutine. A subroutine amounts to a detour in the program that returns to the statement immediately following the one that caused the detour in the first place. This capability permits a set of program statements to be accessed from more than one point in a program. The statement pair GØSUB-RETURN accomplishes this.

One significant use of the subroutine is to improve the flow of control through a program. A subroutine may be used to eliminate the proliferation of GØTØ statements by replacing them with RETURN statements where appropriate. This technique often simplifies the writing of programs. Programs written in this way are also easier to read and thus easier to correct or modify later (see, for example, programs GRAPH2 and GRAPH3 of Chap. 5).

Suppose that we want the product and the sum of two numbers modulo M. We can write a subroutine that calculates and prints both values. Then we can "call" the subroutine from anywhere in the program with GØSUB n where n is the first line of the subroutine. See lines 140 and 210 in program MØD.

```
MØD

94    REM * THIS PROGRAM DEMONSTRATES GOSUB
95    REM  WITH MODULAR ARITHMETIC
99    RANDOMIZE
100   DEF FNR(X) = INT( RND*X+1 )
110   PRINT  "FIND A*B AND A+B MOD M"
120   PRINT  "A,B,M";
130   INPUT A, B, M
→140      GOSUB 500
150   PRINT
160   PRINT  "NOW DO FOUR RANDOM CALCULATIONS"
170   FOR I = 1 TO 4
180     LET M = FNR(9)+1
```

```
190        LET A = FNR(M-1)
200        LET B = FNR(M-1)
210           GOSUB 500
220     NEXT I
222
224     REM * THE STOP STATEMENT PREVENTS
225     REM   ILLEGAL SUBROUTINE ENTRY
230     STOP
492
494     REM * MODULAR ARITHMETIC SUBROUTINE
500     LET P = A*B
510        IF P < M THEN 540
520     LET P = P-M
530     GOTO 510
540     LET S = A+B
550        IF S < M THEN 580
560     LET S = S-M
570     GOTO 550
580     PRINT   A; "*"; B; "="; P; A; "+"; B; "="; S; "MOD"; M
590     RETURN
592
999     END
RUN
MOD

FIND A*B AND A+B MOD M
A,B,M? 2,5,6
  2 * 5 = 4   2 + 5 = 1 MOD 6

NOW DO FOUR RANDOM CALCULATIONS
  3 * 2 = 2   3 + 2 = 1 MOD 4
  2 * 1 = 2   2 + 1 = 3 MOD 5
  1 * 3 = 3   1 + 3 = 4 MOD 8
  2 * 4 = 8   2 + 4 = 6 MOD 9
```

Subroutines may in turn call other subroutines as in both lines 510 and 550 of MOD1. One thing to avoid in subroutines is inadvertent use of variables that have been used elsewhere in the program. Subroutines called from other subroutines are called "nested subroutines." (What else?) In our example MOD1 we have nested them two deep. Systems vary, but many have a limit on how deep subroutines may be nested.

```
MOD1

94      REM * THIS PROGRAM INTRODUCES A NESTED
95      REM   GOSUB INTO PROGRAM MOD
99      RANDOMIZE
100     DEF FNR(X) = INT( RND*X+1 )
110     PRINT   "FIND A*B AND A+B MOD M"
120     PRINT   "A,B,M";
130     INPUT A, B, M
140        GOSUB 500
150     PRINT
160     PRINT   "NOW DO FOUR RANDOM CALCULATIONS"
170     FOR I = 1 TO 4
180        LET M = FNR(9)+1
190        LET A = FNR(M-1)
200        LET B = FNR(M-1)
210           GOSUB 500
220     NEXT I
222
224     REM * THE STOP STATEMENT PREVENTS
225     REM   ILLEGAL SUBROUTINE ENTRY
230     STOP
492
494     REM * MODULAR ARITHMETIC SUBROUTINE
500     LET N = A*B
```

```
  →510      GØSUB 700
   520   LET P = N
   540   LET N = A+B
  →550      GØSUB 700
   560   LET S = N
   580   PRINT  A;  "*";  B;  "=";  P;  A;  "+";  B;  "=";  S;  "MØD";  M
   590   RETURN
   592
   694   REM * REM REDUCES N TO A NUMBER MOD M
   700      IF N < M THEN 730
   710   LET N = N-M
   720   GØTO 700
   730   RETURN
   732
   999   END
   RUN
   MØD 1

   FIND A*B AND A+B MØD M
   A,B,M?  3,4,5
    3 * 4 = 2   3 + 4 = 2 MOD 5

   NØW DØ FØUR RANDOM CALCULATIONS
    2 * 3 = 6   2 + 3 = 5 MOD 8
    4 * 1 = 4   4 + 1 = 5 MOD 9
    2 * 2 = 4   2 + 2 = 4 MOD 6
    6 * 8 = 8   6 + 8 = 4 MOD 10
```

Some systems have a computed GØSUB statement similar in format to the computed GØTØ. The format is:

$$100 \quad \text{ØN K GØSUB } n_1, n_2, n_3, \text{etc.}$$

or

$$100 \quad \text{GØSUB K ØF } n_1, n_2, n_3, \text{etc.}$$

or

$$100 \quad \text{GØSUB } n_1, n_2, n_3, \text{ØN K}$$

## Arrays

An array is simply a two dimensional list. For this we use two subscripts separated by a comma and enclosed in parentheses. The first subscript designates the row and the second subscript designates the column. As with lists, we can use a subscript as high as 10 without the need for a DIM statement.

Suppose you recorded the temperature at 6AM, 12NOON and 6PM for one week. This data could easily be stored in an array to enable a program to carry out various calculations, for example, see program WETHR.

```
   WETHR

   94    REM * THIS PROGRAM FINDS AVERAGE TEMPERATURE
   95    REM  TO DEMONSTRATE A USE OF ARRAYS
   100   DIM A(6,4)
   102
   104   REM * READ DATA
   110   FOR D = 1 TO 5
   120      FOR I = 1 TO 3
   130         READ A(D,I)
   140      NEXT I
   150   NEXT D
   152
```

```
154    REM * CALCULATE AVERAGE EACH DAY
160    FOR D = 1 TO 5
170      LET T = 0
180      FOR I = 1 TO 3
190        LET T = T+A(D,I)
200      NEXT I
210      LET A(D,4) = T/3
220    NEXT D
222
224    REM * CALCULATE AVERAGE EACH READING
230    FOR I = 1 TO 3
240      LET T = 0
250      FOR D = 1 TO 5
260        LET T = T+A(D,I)
270      NEXT D
280      LET A(6,I) = T/5
290    NEXT I
292
300    PRINT  "DAY\TIME", "6AM", "12NOON", "6PM", "DAILY AVG"
310    PRINT
320    FOR D = 1 TO 5
322
324      REM * KEEP TERMINAL ON THIS LINE
325      REM FOR THE NEXT PRINTED RESULT
326      REM WITH TRAILING COMMA IN LINE 330
330      PRINT  "DAY"; D,
340      FOR I = 1 TO 3
350        PRINT A(D,I),
360      NEXT I
370      PRINT A(D,4)
380    NEXT D
382
390    FOR I = 1 TO 50
400      PRINT  "-";
410    NEXT I
420    PRINT
422
430    PRINT  "AVERAGES",
440    FOR I = 1 TO 3
450      PRINT A(6,I),
460    NEXT I
470    PRINT
472
474    REM
480    DATA  27,36,34,  40,50,55,  50,52,48
490    DATA  43,41,37,  30,33,28
500    END
RUN
WETHR
```

| DAY\TIME | 6AM | 12NOON | 6PM | DAILY AVG |
|---|---|---|---|---|
| DAY 1 | 27 | 36 | 34 | 32.3333 |
| DAY 2 | 40 | 50 | 55 | 48.3333 |
| DAY 3 | 50 | 52 | 48 | 50 |
| DAY 4 | 43 | 41 | 37 | 40.3333 |
| DAY 5 | 30 | 33 | 28 | 30.3333 |
| ---------------------------------------------------------- | | | | |
| AVERAGES | 38 | 42.4 | 40.4 | |

Even though the computer permits a subscript as high as 10 for rows and for columns, it does not require that we use them all. In WETHR we used only six rows and four columns.

Note that we used loops within loops, or nested loops, several times in WETHR. The requirement here is that the loops must be nested entirely within other loops.  If a program contains FØR X = A TØ B followed by FØR Y = C TØ D, the NEXT Y statement must appear before the NEXT X statement.

Once the data is stored, it is a simple matter to obtain other information. For example, we can find the highest temperature reading for the week as in WETHR1.

```
WETHR1

94    REM * THIS PRØGRAM FINDS HIGHEST TEMPERATURE
95    REM   IN A FIVE DAY PERIØD USING ARRAYS
100   DIM A(6,4)
102
104   REM * READ DATA
110   FØR D = 1 TØ 5
120      FØR I = 1 TØ 3
130         READ A(D,I)
140      NEXT I
150   NEXT D
152
154   REM * THE FIRST ENTRY IS THE HIGHEST SØ FAR
160   LET H = A(1,1)
170   LET R = C = 1
180   FØR D = 1 TØ 5
190      FØR I = 1 TØ 3
200            IF A(D,I) <= H THEN 240
202
204            REM * IF THE CURRENT ENTRY IS HIGHER THEN
205            REM   SAVE DATA IN H, R, AND C
210            LET H = A(D,I)
220            LET R = D
230            LET C = I
240      NEXT I
250   NEXT D
252
260   PRINT  "HIGHEST TEMPERATURE ="; H
262
264   REM * USE ØF 24-HØUR CLOCK SIMPLIFIES.
265   REM   PRINTING THE TIME
270   PRINT   "ØCCURS AT"; C*600; "HØURS ON DAY"; R
474   REM
480   DATA   27,36,34,   40,50,55,   50,52,48
490   DATA   43,41,37,   30,33,28
500   END
RUN
WETHR1

HIGHEST TEMPERATURE = 55
ØCCURS AT 1800    HØURS ØN DAY ?
```

## Summary of Sec. 1-4

BASIC allows tremendous flexibility in the user defined functions.  We may have up to 26 functions defined with DEF FNA(X) followed by an equals sign and any legal BASIC formula.

For calculations that don't lend themselves to function definition, such as calculations requiring more than one value in the result, the subroutine entered with GØSUB is available.  The end of a subroutine is indicated by the RETURN statement.

Two dimensional variables are available in BASIC.  A(I,J) designates the Ith row and the Jth column of A.  For subscripts greater than 10, a DIM state-ment is required.

## Problems for Sec. 1-4

1) Write a program to read six test scores for each of five students into an array, one student to a row. Find the test average by student and by test, and print the scores and the results in easily readable form.

2) Write a program to locate the maximum and the minimum point of any function in a domain specified as input. Also specify the increments as input.

3) Write a program to set up a tic-tac-toe board and keep track of the play of two external players.

4) Write a program to fill a square array with zeros except along the diagonal from the upper left to the lower right corners, which should contain ones. Print this array (called the "identity array").

5) Write a program to produce the results of program CØMPAR in Sec. 1-1 using a simple GØSUB and only one GØTØ.

6) Write a program to produce the results of program CØMPAR in Sec. 1-1 using SGN(A – B) and the computed GØSUB.

7) If your system allows two arguments in user defined functions, write a single function to allow rounding off numbers to any desired precision. Try the same thing with a single argument function. Write a program to verify your functions.

## 1-5  MAT Statements in BASIC

Arrays and lists are used so routinely in programming and in mathematics applications that most implementations of BASIC include a group of special statements to handle them. Note that since BASIC treats lists as special arrays, we may not use the same letter for a one-dimensional list that we use for a two-dimensional array. Instead of reading values into the elements of an array entry by entry with loops, we may simply use MAT  READ A or MAT  READ A, B,C as long as the array or the arrays are dimensioned to be compatible with the data. BASIC also allows us to alter the dimensions of arrays in the MAT READ statement. MAT  READ A,B(3,7),C(N,M) reads mat A according to previously set dimensions; dimensions B to three rows and seven columns; reads the array and dimensions C to N rows and M columns, N and M having been previously defined; and reads that array.

MAT  PRINT A prints the complete array with comma format. To get semicolon format, MAT PRINT A; must be used. A single statement may specify printing of more than one array, as in MAT  PRINT A,B;C, which will result in A being printed with comma spacing, followed by B printed with semicolon spacing, followed by C printed with comma spacing (see program MAT01).

MAT INPUT allows us to type entries from the keyboard of our terminal with all of the dimensioning options of MAT READ. MAT INPUT A has one additional option in some implementations of BASIC. If A is a list, you may not know the number of entries required when the program is written. In some systems, the function NUM takes on the number of elements entered in the most recent MAT  INPUT statement in the program.

MATO1

```
 94   REM * THIS PROGRAM DEMONSTRATES
 95   REM   MAT   READ AND MAT   PRINT
100   DIM A(3,4), B(6,10), C(8,9)
110   READ R,C
120   MAT   READ   A, B(2,5), C(R,C)
130   MAT   PRINT A, B; C
132   REM
140   DATA  4,3
150   DATA  1,2,3,4,5,6,7,8,9,10,11,12
160   DATA  13,14,15,16,17,18,19,20,21,22
170   DATA  23,24,25,26,27,28,29,30,31,32,33,34
180   END
RUN
MATO1
```

| 1  | 2  | 3  | 4  |
|----|----|----|----|
| 5  | 6  | 7  | 8  |
| 9  | 10 | 11 | 12 |

| 13 | 14 | 15 | 16 | 17 |
|----|----|----|----|----|
| 18 | 19 | 20 | 21 | 22 |

| 23 | 24 | 25 |
|----|----|----|
| 26 | 27 | 28 |
| 29 | 30 | 31 |
| 32 | 33 | 34 |

Other statements that may be used to assign values to the elements of arrays are as follows:

| MAT A = ZER | Fills array A with zeros according to previously specified dimensions. |
|-------------|-----------------------------------------------------------------------|
| MAT A = ZER(2,3) | Redimensions A and fills it with zeros. |
| MAT A = ZER (B,C) | Redimensions A and fills it with zeros. |
| MAT A = ZER(5) | Redimensions A and fills it with zeros. |
| MAT A = ZER(X) | Redimensions A and fills it with zeros. |

MAT A = CØN fills the array A with ones. As shown, the dimensions must have been previously determined. CØN has all of the redimensioning options shown for ZER.

MAT A = IDN is used only for a square array (where the number of rows is equal to the number of columns). A is filled with ones where the row number and the column number are equal and all other locations are set equal to zero. IDN may be redimensioned with IDN(X,X) or IDN(5,5). This is called the "identity matrix" in matrix algebra.

In matrix algebra, addition and subtraction are defined for like-dimensioned arrays as the sum or difference, respectively, of elements having the same location. That is, if array X is the sum or difference of Y and Z, then for all I,J we have $X(I,J) = Y(I,J) \pm Z(I,J)$. This could be done with nested loops; in BASIC, however, we merely type:

$$100 \quad \text{MAT X} = \text{Y} + \text{Z} \qquad \text{for addition}$$
$$100 \quad \text{MAT X} = \text{Y} - \text{Z} \qquad \text{for subtraction}$$

Matrix multiplication has a more complicated definition. For arrays Y and Z, the number of columns in Y must equal the number of rows in Z. The (R,C)th entry of X is the sum of the products Y(R,T)*Z(T,C), where T goes from one to the number of columns in Y, which is also the number of rows in Z. The product matrix will have the same number of columns as X and the same number of rows as Y. A BASIC program for matrix multiplication requires triple nested loops.

The following statement accomplishes the same result:

$$100 \quad \text{MAT X} = \text{Y}*\text{Z}$$

Note that if multiplication works for Y*Z, it will work for Z*Y only if the arrays are square. In any case, the product has the number of rows of the left multiplier and the number of columns of the right multiplier (see program MAT02).

In matrix algebra, instead of dividing Y by Z, we first find the inverse of Z. The inverse of Z, written $Z^{-1}$, is the matrix such that $Z*Z^{-1}$ equals the

```
MAT02

100    DIM  X(10,10), Y(10,10), Z(10,10), P(10,10)
102
104    REM * READ MATRIX DIMENSIONS
110    READ I,J, K,L
120       IF J = K THEN 150
130    PRINT  "PRODUCT UNDEFINED"
140    STOP
142
144    REM * READ MATRIX ELEMENTS
150    MAT   READ Y(I,J), Z(K,L)
152
154    REM * INITIALIZE PRODUCT MATRIX
160    MAT X = ZER(I,L)
162
164    REM * MULTIPLY USING NESTED LOOPS
170    FOR T = 1 TO J
180       FOR R = 1 TO I
190          FOR C = 1 TO L
200             LET X(R,C) = X(R,C)+Y(R,T)*Z(T,C)
210          NEXT C
220       NEXT R
230    NEXT T
232
240    PRINT  "USING TRIPLE NESTED LOOPS"
250    MAT   PRINT X;
260    PRINT
262
264    REM * DEMONSTRATE MAT PRODUCT IN BASIC
270    MAT P = ZER(I,L)
280    MAT P = Y*Z
290    PRINT  "USING MAT MULTIPLY STATEMENT"
300    MAT   PRINT P;
302
304    REM
310    DATA  2,3,  3,4
320    DATA  1,2,3,4,5,6
330    DATA  1,2,3,4,5,6,7,8,9,10,11,12
340    END
```

```
RUN
MATO2

USING TRIPLE NESTED LOOPS
   38      44     50     56

   83      98    113    128


USING MAT MULTIPLY STATEMENT
   38      44     50     56

   83      98    113    128
```

identity matrix. Having found the inverse of Z, we multiply Y by it. The inverse (if it exists) is obtained with the following statement:

$$100 \quad \text{MAT X} = \text{INV(Z)}$$

BASIC allows us to find the transpose of a matrix with the following statement:

$$100 \quad \text{MAT X} = \text{TRN(Z)}$$

The transpose consists of an array X such that the columns of X are the rows of Z and the rows of X are the columns of Z. Note that if the dimensions of Z are (R,C), then the dimensions of X must be (C,R).

We can duplicate an array with

$$.100 \quad \text{MAT X} = \text{Z}$$

and can multiply every entry of an array by the same number with

$$100 \quad \text{MAT X} = \text{(C)*Z}$$

where C is any legal BASIC formula.

In the last seven cases just presented, some systems use the statement itself to dimension or redimension X, whereas others require that the program make the dimensions of X compatible in advance.

## Summary

BASIC provides a number of MAT statements that greatly simplify programs which deal with arrays. They are as follows:

| | |
|---|---|
| MAT READ | Reads data into a variable list. |
| MAT INPUT | Enters data from the keyboard into a variable list. |
| MAT X = ZER | Fills X with zeros. |
| MAT X = CØN | Fills X with ones. |
| MAT X = IDN | Creates the identity matrix. |
| MAT PRINT | Prints the contents of a variable list to the terminal. |
| MAT X = Y | Copies the contents of Y into X. |
| MAT X = Y + Z | Enters the sum of Y and Z into X. |
| MAT X = Y - Z | Enters the difference of Y and Z into X. |
| MAT X = Y*Z | Enters the product of Y and Z into X. |
| MAT X = (C)*Y | Multiplies each entry of Y by C and enters result in X. |

MAT X  =  INV(Y)      Enters the inverse of Y into X.
MAT X = TRN(Y)      Enters the transpose of Y into X.

The first five statements above have optional redimensioning capabilities.

## Problems For 1-5

1) Write a program to add or subtract two arrays without using matrix statements from this section.
2) Write a program to enter 25 random integers into a five by five array and print it.  Now find the largest number in each row and its column number, and find the largest number in each column and its row number.
3) Write a program to print a times table modulo six.
4) Write a program to print a times table modulo five.
5) MAT  READ the integers one through nine into a three by three array. Copy this into the upper left corner of a four by four array.  Use the fourth row to enter the column sums, and use the fourth column to enter the row sums.  Print the resulting array.
6) Write a program to create the transpose of a given matrix without using the TRN function.

# 2
# SOME EXTENDED
# FEATURES OF BASIC

## 2-1 Introduction

None of the features to be discussed in this chapter is absolutely necessary to writing programs in BASIC. Other language statements may be assembled to achieve the same effect of each one. Some of them may not even be available on the computer you are using. However, if your system does provide any of the features presented here, you are encouraged to experiment since they save programming effort and storage space and make programs more readable.

(Note about problems: The author has not attempted to contrive problems which would require the reader to use the various features presented in this chapter. Rather it is recommended that you be alert to possibilities for using the material of this chapter in programs you will be writing throughout the rest of the book.)

## 2-2 TAB

The TAB(X) function is available on many BASIC systems. TAB(X) placed in a PRINT statement causes the printing mechanism of the terminal to be located in the $x^{th}$ space of the current line, provided it has not already passed that point. Note that on most systems the leftmost space is numbered zero and the counting is modular, with the mod being typically 72 or 75, but sometimes more. Some systems are not modular but start on a new line when the TAB argument exceeds the system line length. An explicit number or BASIC formula may be entered as the argument of the TAB function. If the value of the argument is not an integer, most systems use only the integer part. See program TAB01.

```
TAB01

94    REM * PRINT SCALE TO AID COUNTING SPACES
100   FOR I = 1 TO 5
110      FOR J = 1 TO 9
120         PRINT "-";
130      NEXT J
140      PRINT "!";
150   NEXT I
160   PRINT
162
164   REM * PRINT IN LOCATIONS READ FROM DATA
170   FOR K = 1 TO 5
180      READ T
190      PRINT  TAB(T); "X";
200   NEXT K
210   PRINT
212
214   REM * SHOW TAB MORE THAN ONCE IN
215   REM   THE SAME PRINT STATEMENT
220   READ A, B, C
230   PRINT  TAB(A); "A"; TAB(B); "B"; TAB(C); "C"
234   REM
240   DATA   3, 8, 12, 28, 48
250   DATA   2, 7, 15
260   END
RUN
TAB01

---------!---------!---------!---------!---------!
   X     X   X                     X                        X
   A     B   C
```

Examining the output of program TAB01 and counting the leftmost space as zero, we see that the X's are printed in the spaces numbered 3, 8, 12, 28, and 48, as designated in the DATA of line 240.

The uses of the TAB function are not limited to literal output. We may also format numeric output or a mixture of numeric and literal output. See program TAB02.

```
TAB02

94    REM * TAB DEMONSTRATION PROGRAM
100   DIM A(4)
102
104   REM * READ FOUR ITEM A LIST
110   FOR I = 1 TO 4
120      READ A(I)
130   NEXT I
132
140   PRINT  TAB(15); "COMMA SPACING"
150   FOR I = 1 TO 4
160      PRINT  A(I),
170   NEXT I
180   PRINT
182
190   PRINT TAB(10); "USING TAB FOR 10 CHARACTER PRINT ZONE
200   FOR I = 1 TO 4
210      PRINT  TAB( 10*(I-1) ); A(I);
220   NEXT I
230   PRINT
232
240   PRINT TAB(6); "SEMICOLON SPACING"
250   FOR I = 1 TO 4
260      PRINT  A(I);
270   NEXT I
280   PRINT
```

```
282
290    REM
300    DATA    -3,11,0,406
310    END
RUN
TAB02

                COMMA SPACING
-3              11              0              406
        USING TAB FOR 10 CHARACTER PRINT ZONES
-3              11         0         406
        SEMICOLON SPACING
-3    11   0   406
```

Note that systems differ in the number of spaces generated by the comma and semicolon delimiters.

## 2-3  Print Using

While it is possible with the string facilities available in BASIC (see Chapter 3) to print output in any desired form, formatting can require tedious programming. It is for this reason that many systems provide PRINT USING and image statements.

PRINT USING permits the format for printing output for the current line to be specified in yet another line. The specifications for printing are called the image. The image can be defined in an image statement, which begins with a colon. Very simply, a pound sign is used to specify where we want digits printed. For pound signs placed to the right of the decimal point, zeros to the right of the last nonzero digit are printed. For pound signs placed to the left of the decimal point, zeros to the left of the leading nonzero digit are not printed.

One of the common uses of PRINT USING is to obtain zeros to the right of the decimal point in printed output, since as a numeric the trailing zero is dropped in BASIC. If we want $3.10 printed, we may use an image to force the printing of the zero, as shown in our first demonstration program, IMAGE01.

```
IMAGE01

94     REM  * DEMONSTRATES ELEMENTARY
95     REM    EXAMPLE FOR PRINT USING
100    LET D = 3.1
110    PRINT   "THIS IS WITHOUT IMAGE"
120    PRINT   "THE AMOUNT IS $"; D
130    PRINT
140    PRINT   "THIS IS WITH IMAGE"
150    :THE AMOUNT IS $##.##
160    PRINT USING 150, D
170    END
RUN
IMAGE01

THIS IS WITHOUT IMAGE
THE AMOUNT IS $ 3.1

THIS IS WITH IMAGE
THE AMOUNT IS $ 3.10
```

Next we present program IMAGE02 to show a variety of numbers printed in a variety of images.

```
IMAGE02

94    REM * DEMONSTRATES A VARIETY CF IMAGES
100   : $$$##.###   ###.##    ####.     ####    ##      #
102
110   FOR I = 1 TO 5
120      READ X
130      PRINT   "THE NUMBER IS"; X
140      PRINT USING 100, X, X, X, X, X, X
150      PRINT
160   NEXT I
162
164   REM
170   DATA 1, 12, 12.3, 1234.56, .01
180   END
RUN
IMAGE02

THE NUMBER IS 1
  $ 1.000     1.00      1.        1      1       1

THE NUMBER IS 12
  $12.000     12.00     12.      12     12      *12

THE NUMBER IS 12.3
  $12.300     12.30     12.      12     12      *12

THE NUMBER IS 1234.56
$1234.560   *1234.56  1235.    1234   *1234    *1234

THE NUMBER IS 0.01
  $ .010      .01       0.        0      0       0
```

Note that where several dollar signs appear only one of them gets printed. The one that is printed is as far right as possible in a space that has a dollar sign in the image. When there is not room to the right of the decimal point in the image to print all of the digits, the excess is dropped. No rounding off is done. Where there is not room to the left, all digits get printed anyway, and an asterisk is printed to call attention to the fact that the number did not fit the image.

The image can be a string. In this case, the line number which calls the image in the PRINT USING statement is replaced by the string variable that contains the image, as in program IMAGE03.

```
IMAGE03

94    REM * DEMONSTRATES IMAGE STORED
95    REM   IN A STRING VARIABLE
100   LET IS = "###.##      $$$#.##"
110   LET N = 23.4
120   PRINT   N; " IS THE NUMBER"
130   PRINT   IS; " IS THE IMAGE"
140   PRINT   USING IS, N, N
150   END
RUN
IMAGE03

  23.4  IS THE NUMBER
###.##      $$$#.## IS THE IMAGE
  23.40      $23.40
```

We can force the computer to print numeric output using E-format. Four up arrows are used for this, as shown in program IMAGE04.

```
IMAGE04

94    REM * PRINTS E-FØRMAT
100   : ##.##↑↑↑↑
110   LET N = 24.3
120   PRINT USING 100, N
130   PRINT N; "IS THE NUMBER"
140   END
RUN
IMAGE04

   2.43E+01
24.3 IS THE NUMBER
```

Strings may be formatted with images also. An apostrophe must be used to begin the printing for a string image. Then control letters E, L, R, and C may be used to indicate fields of specific characteristics. Control character E calls for left justification and allows the string to overflow, whereas L calls for left justification but truncates on the right. Control character R calls for right justification and truncates any excess, and C calls for centering the string output and truncates on the right if there is an excess. The apostrophe is needed to delimit the control characters because any other alphabetic characters will be printed just as they appear in the image. See program IMAGE05 for a demonstration of formatting string output in the image.

```
IMAGE05

94    REM * DEMONSTRATES PRINTING STRINGS
95    REM  USING AN IMAGE STRING
100   LET I$ = " 'LLLL      'RRRRR       'CCCCC      'EE"
110   PRINT I$
120   FØR I = 1 TØ 5
130      READ S$
140      PRINT USING I$, S$, S$, S$, S$
150   NEXT I
152
154   REM
160   DATA  THIS, IS, A, SAMPLE, PRØGRAM
170   END
RUN
IMAGE05

'LLLL        'RRRRR       'CCCCC      'EE
THIS         THIS         THIS        THIS
IS           IS           IS          IS
A            A            A           A
SAMPL        SAMPLE       SAMPLE      SAMPLE
PRØGR        PRØGRA       PRØGRA      PRØGRAM
```

## 2-4   Logical Operations, MAX and MIN

### Truth Values

Some BASIC implementations include a set of logical operations. Let's look at the already familiar IF-THEN statement. The statement IF X=1 THEN 200 transfers control to line 200 only if X=1 is true. If X=1 is true, BASIC assigns the statement X=1 a value of 1 to designate 'true.' If X=1 is false, then BASIC assigns it a value of 0 to designate 'false.' So we could replace our program statement with IF X THEN 200, and when X=1 the computer goes to 200; otherwise control passes to the next line in sequence, provided X can be only 0 or 1.

We may even print the logical value of statements. If we print the value of N/X=INT(N/X), we should get a one when X is a factor of N and a zero when X is not a factor of N (see line 150 of program LØGIC1).

```
LØGIC1

94   REM * THIS PRØGRAM DEMØNSTRATES THE TRUTH VALUE
95   REM  ØF THE STATEMENT N/X = INT(N/X)
100    PRINT "INPUT N";
110    INPUT N
114    REM * PRINT HEADINGS
120    PRINT "X","N/X","INT(N/X)","TRUTH VALUE ØF"
130    PRINT TAB(45);"N/X = INT(N/X)"
140    FØR X=1 TØ N
→150   PRINT X,N/X,INT(N/X),N/X=INT(N/X)
160    NEXT X
170    END
RUN
LØGIC1

INPUT N?6
X                 N/X              INT(N/X)         TRUTH VALUE ØF
                                                    N/X = INT(N/X)
1                 6                6                1
2                 3                3                1
3                 2                2                1
4                 1.5              1                0
5                 1.2              1                0
6                 1                1                1
```

The fourth column prints the logical value of N/X=INT(N/X). As we expected, that value is one whenever X is a factor of N and zero whenever X is not a factor of N. This gives us a novel approach for counting factors of N. See line 140 of program LØGIC2. Where available, all of the relational operators may be used in a similar manner.

```
LØGIC2

94   REM * THIS PRØGRAM COUNTS FACTORS ØF INTEGERS
95   REM  USING THE TRUTH VALUE ØF N/X = INT(N/X)
100    PRINT "INPUT AN INTEGER";
110    INPUT N
120    LET T=0
130    FØR X=1 TØ N
→140   LET T=T+(N/X=INT(N/X))
150    NEXT X
160    PRINT T;"FACTØRS"
170    END
RUN
LØGIC2

INPUT AN INTEGER?240
  20    FACTØRS

RUN
LØGIC2

INPUT AN INTEGER?1949
   2    FACTØRS
```

## Logical Operators

The logical operators AND, ØR, and NØT are available on some BASIC systems and may be used in a wide variety of applications. One rather straightforward application is an extension of IF-THEN statements. We may often combine several IF-THEN's into one statement. For example, the pair,

```
100   IF  X=3  THEN  200
110   IF  Y<2  THEN  200
```

becomes

```
100   IF  X=3  OR  Y<2  THEN  200
```

Or the four statements,

```
100   IF  X  <>  3  THEN  130
110   IF  Y  >=  2  THEN  130
120   GØTØ  510
130   PRINT  "MESSAGE"
```

become

```
100   IF  X=3  AND  Y<2  THEN  510
110   PRINT  "MESSAGE"
```

We can negate a statement with NØT. That is, X<>3 and NØT(X=3) are equivalent. (When you are unsure of the order of operations, it may be best to use parentheses if only to make the statement easier to read.) What about X and NØT X? In this case, X is either equal to zero or it isn't. So in the case IF NØT X THEN 200, control passes to line 200 for X=0 (because NØT 0 equals 1) and passes to the next statement in sequence for all other values.

## MAX and MIN

For a system which provides MAX and MIN functions, the value of A MAX B becomes the larger of the two numbers. The value of A MIN B becomes the smaller of the two numbers. If you don't have these functions, then you may use

.5*(A+B−ABS(A−B)) for A MIN B and .5*(A+B+ABS(A−B)) for A MAX B

## 2-5  Multiple Line Defined Function

Some versions of BASIC provide multiple line user-defined functions that permit defining of functions that require two or more program statements to define. The first line must be DEF FN followed by the function identifying letter and the function argument or arguments in parentheses. The last statement must be FNEND, and in between there must be at least one assignment statement with FN and the same letter specified in the DEF statement on the left of the equals sign.

For example, we may write a multiple line function that will do modular multiplication. The function of lines 100 through 160 in program FUNCTIØN does just that.

As with other user defined functions, the multiple line function may be accessed at any point of the program. In this way we may often save program space, just as GØSUB is often used to avoid repeating a set of program statements. However, the defined function is accessed directly whenever its name is used and thus it does not require a special statement to transfer control to it. The defined function may be used in all situations where a single value is required for each parameter or set of parameters, whereas a subroutine is more appropriate if two or more variables must be returned.

```
FUNCTION

94    REM * THIS PROGRAM DEMONSTRATES A USE OF THE
95    REM   MULTIPLE LINE USER DEFINED FUNCTION
96
97    REM * THE FUNCTION IS DEFINED IN LINES 100 THROUGH 160
100   DEF FNM(X,Y,Z)
110   LET P = X*Y
120      IF  P < Z THEN 150
130   LET P = P-Z
140   GOTO 120
150   LET FNM = P
160   FNEND
192
200   PRINT "MULTIPLY A TIMES B MOD M TO GET"
210   READ A, B, M
220      IF M = 0 THEN 260
230   PRINT  TAB(8); A; TAB(16); B; TAB(22); M; TAB(27); FNM(A,
240   GOTO 210
242
244   REM
250   DATA 1,2,3,  3,2,4,  3,3,4,  0,0,0
260   END
RUN
FUNCTION

MULTIPLY A TIMES B MOD M TO GET
       1        2        3        2
       3        2        4        2
       3        3        4        1
```

# 3
# STRINGS

## 3-1 Introduction

A string is simply any set of characters that is not to be treated as a number but is to be otherwise manipulated by the computer. The characters are referred to as alphameric or alphanumeric, since both alphabetic and numeric symbols may be used, as are most other symbols permitted by your terminal, even including the nonprinting characters. It is the purpose of this chapter to outline a few of the possible uses of strings and string variables in BASIC even though the specifications are not uniform from system to system. The user should determine the capabilities of his or her own system before planning extensive programming activity.

## 3-2 The String Simple Variable

To distinguish the string variable from the numeric variable, virtually all systems use a trailing dollar sign ($) in the variable name for a string. Legal simple string variable names are A$, K$, B3$, and C8$. Some systems are restricted to the 26 letters of the alphabet, not permitting such variables as B3$. Others allow additional variables such as &$. The number of characters you are allowed to store in one simple string varies typically from 18 to thousands. Most of the manipulations allowed for numeric variables are allowed for string variables except for arithmetic operations. String variables can be READ, INPUT, assigned, printed, and compared for order. Order comparison is accomplished according to ASCII (American Standard Code for Information Interchange) specifications, which place the digits in order 0 through 9 ahead of the letters of the alphabet in alphabetical order. (See Appendix A for relevant parts of the code.)

One of the uses of strings is to permit person-computer "conversation." We do not need to numerically code our answers to questions put to the program user. If we wish to give the program operator options, the answers can be words which the computer processes directly. If for example, we write a program that will require a lot of yes-no answers from the keyboard, we may write

31

a subroutine that prints the question, checks the answer to be sure that it is either a "YES" or a "NØ," and rerequests the answer for all other responses.

Program DECIDE uses such a subroutine repeatedly as the computer assembles the information fed into it by the user. The subroutine outlined above begins in line 800.

```
DECIDE
    94   REM * DEMONSTRATION PROGRAM INTRODUCING STRINGS
    95   REM   SHOWS ASSIGNMENT, INPUT, COMPARISION AND
    96   REM   PRINTING OF STRINGS
   100   GOSUB 200
   110   LET X$ = Q$
   120   GOSUB 400
   130   LET Y$ = Q$
   140   PRINT   "PROGRAM NAME";
   150   INPUT   N$
   160   PRINT
→  170   PRINT   X$; Y$; " - "; N$
   180   STOP
   192
   194   REM * LANGUAGE DECISION SUBROUTINE
   200   LET Q$ = "FORTRAN"
   210   GOSUB 800
   220      IF A$ = "YES" THEN 310
   230   LET Q$ = "COBOL"
   240   GOSUB 800
   250      IF A$ = "YES" THEN 310
   260   LET Q$ = "BASIC"
   270   GOSUB 800
   280      IF A$ = "YES" THEN 310
   290   PRINT "FORTRAN, COBOL OR BASIC ONLY"
   300   GOTO 200
   310   RETURN
   392
   394   REM * MAKE 'OLD - NEW' DECISION HERE
   400   LET Q$ = " OLD"
   410   GOSUB 800
   420      IF A$ = "YES" THEN 480
   430   LET Q$ = " NEW"
   440   GOSUB 800
   450      IF A$ = "YES" THEN 480
   460   PRINT   "OLD OR NEW ONLY"
   470   GOTO 400
   480   RETURN
   782
   784   REM * YES-NO DECISION SUBROUTINE
   785   REM   ENTER WITH GOSUB 800
   790   PRINT   "YES OR NO"
→  800   PRINT   Q$;
   810   INPUT   A$
   820      IF A$ = "YES" THEN 850
   830      IF A$ = "NO" THEN 850
   840   GOTO 790
   850   RETURN
   999   END
RUN
DECIDE

FORTRAN?NO
COBOL?NO
BASIC?YES
 OLD?YES
PROGRAM NAME?DECIDE

BASIC OLD - DECIDE
```

Strings are read from data in exactly the same manner that numerics are read from data. String and numeric data may be intermixed. Some systems require that string data be enclosed in quotes. On systems that do not require quotes, any expression that contains a comma will have to be enclosed in quotes anyway, since the comma will otherwise be interpreted as the end of the string.

Look at line 170 of program DECIDE. Note that the string variables are separated by semicolon delimiters in that PRINT statement. You should see that the printed output has no spaces other than those actually placed in string Y$ and the literal expression " - " by the program itself. When printing numeric values, the computer always provides some space automatically when using semicolons as delimiters. When printing strings, the computer does not provide any space automatically. We can print string characters right next to each other by using semicolons. We can print strings in 15-character columns using commas, or we can use the TAB function for other spacing. Some systems also provide PRINT USING for yet another formatting capability.

We can easily construct a program to do for two strings exactly what program CØMPAR in Sec. 1-2 did for two numerics, as shown in program CØMPR$. All we want is to determine if A$ is less than, greater than, or equal to B$. Look carefully to see what happens to the leading and trailing blanks in the strings. In this case, the leading blank makes " ALPHA" less than "ALPHA", but the trailing blank in "BETA " has no effect. Some systems will not ignore trailing blanks. Also note that the string 0123456789 is placed in quotes. When calling for a string read, some computers will ignore such a string unless it is in quotes because it 'looks like' a numeric.

```
COMPR$

94    REM * THIS PROGRAM COMPARES TWO
95    REM   STRINGS FØR ORDER
100   READ A$, B$
110      IF A$ = "STOP" THEN 260
120      IF A$ = B$ THEN 160
130      IF A$ < B$ THEN 180
140   PRINT   A$; " IS GREATER THAN "; B$
150   GØTØ 100
160   PRINT   A$; " IS EQUAL TO "; B$
170   GØTO 100
180   PRINT   A$; " IS LESS THAN "; B$
190   GCTC 100
192
194   REM
200   DATA   NUMERIC, ALPHABETIC
210   DATA   "0123456789", ABCDEFGHIJK
→220  DATA   " ALPHA", "ALPHA"
→230  DATA   "BETA ", "BETA"
240   DATA   END, END
250   DATA   STØP, STØP
260   END
RUN
COMPR$

NUMERIC IS GREATER THAN ALPHABETIC
0123456789 IS LESS THAN ABCDEFGHIJK
→ ALPHA IS LESS THAN ALPHA
→BETA  IS EQUAL TØ BETA
END IS EQUAL TØ END
```

## Summary of Sec. 3-2

We have seen that the simple string variable can be used in BASIC programs in many of the same ways that simple numeric variables can. We may use simple string variables in READ, DATA, INPUT, PRINT, and IF-THEN statements. In DATA and INPUT statements, some systems require quotes to delimit strings under certain conditions.

## Problems for Sec. 3-2

1) Write a program to find the highest and lowest ranking strings in a set of data.
2) Write a program that reads two strings and then prints them in ascending order.
3) Write a program that will read three strings from data and print them in ascending order (more on ordering strings later).
4) How many print statements would be required to print n strings in alphabetical order using only the methods of this section?
5) Write a program to request two peoples' names in two strings for each person, first name first. Then have the names printed in alphabetical order. Be sure to handle William Smith and George Smith properly.

## 3-3  The String Subscripted Variable

It is at this point that we must distinguish the ways in which various systems treat subscripted string variables. There are two fundamentally distinct ways to deal with A$(I,J) and B$(I). (Some systems don't even permit the double subscript.)

One concept, as shown in demonstration program ARRAY$, considers A$(I,J) as an element of a string array just as A(I,J) is an element of a numeric

```
ARRAYS

94    REM * THIS PROGRAM IS A DEMONSTRATION OF
95    REM   A STRING ARRAY
96
97    REM * HERE THE DIMENSION SPECIFIES THE NUMBER
98    REM   OF STRINGS THAT MAY BE STORED IN A LIST
100   DIM A$(3)
102
104   REM * READ THE STRING LIST FROM DATA
110   FOR I = 1 TO 3
120      READ A$(I)
130   NEXT I
132
134   REM * NOW PRINT THE STRING LIST
140   FOR I = 1 TO 3
150      PRINT "A$("; I; ") = "; A$(I)
160   NEXT I
172
174   REM
180   DATA  FIRST, SECOND, THIRD
190   END
RUN
ARRAY$

A$( 1 ) = FIRST
A$( 2 ) = SECOND
A$( 3 ) = THIRD
```

array. This makes B$(I) the Ith element of a string list called B$ which may contain up to 11 strings before the DIMension statement is required.

The other concept, as shown in program SUBSTR, considers A$(I,J) as a substring having J−I+1 characters going from the Ith to the Jth character inclusive. So A$(I,I) is the single Ith character. Using this concept, B$(I) is the substring beginning with the Ith character and continuing to the end of the string.

The next two sections will treat these two concepts separately.

```
SUBSTR

94   REM  * THIS PROGRAM IS A DEMONSTRATION
95   REM    OF A$(I,J) AS A SUBSTRING
96   REM
97   REM  * IN THIS CASE THE DIMENSION SPECIFIES THE
98   REM    NUMBER OF CHARACTERS IN THE STRING VARIABLE A$
100  DIM A$[14]
110  LET A$="THIS IS A TEST"
120  PRINT "A$ = ";A$
130  FOR I=1 TO 14 STEP 4
140  LET J=I+INT(RND(-1)*4+1)
150  PRINT "A$(";I;",";J;") = '";A$[I,J];"'"
160  NEXT I
164  REM
170  END
RUN
SUBSTR

A$ = THIS IS A TEST
A$( 1    , 4    ) = 'THIS'
A$( 5    , 6    ) = ' I'
A$( 9    , 12   ) = 'A TE'
A$( 13   , 17   ) = 'ST  '
```

## 3-4   The Substring Scheme*

One advantage in the substring concept is that we can deal with any part or parts of the string directly. One disadvantage is that we cannot deal with hundreds or thousands of strings without the use of files. Strings may be read from data. When placed in data, strings must be enclosed in quotes. The same is true if we type more than one string to the keyboard in response to an INPUT statement.

Generally speaking, the DIMension statement is required for string variables to permit the computer to allocate space. For example, 100 DIM A$(10), B$(58),A(15) provides for 10 characters in A$, 58 characters in B$, and 15 numerics in the A list, the latter showing that string and numeric dimensioning may be intermixed.

A program to arrange the letters of a string in alphabetical order is shown in program ALPHA. Line 100 provides for up to 72 characters in the string variable A$. Line 120 uses the LEN( ) function. This function measures the actual number of characters in the string. Note that lines 160, 170, and 180 exchange two characters which are not in the proper order. Since B$ is used for only a single character, it need not appear in the DIMension statement. Note that spaces have a lower ASCII code than the letter A and so appear first in the result of program ALPHA.

*The programs of Sec. 3-4 were run on a Hewlett Packard Computer.

```
ALPHA

94   REM * THIS PROGRAM ALPHABETIZES THE
95   REM   CHARACTERS OF A STRING
→100  DIM A$[72]
110  INPUT A$
→120  LET L=LEN(A$)
122  REM
124  REM * LINE 150 TESTS ALL POSSIBLE PAIRS OF
125  REM   CHARACTERS TO SEE IF THEY ARE IN ORDER
130  FOR I=1 TO L-1
140  FOR J=I+1 TO L
150  IF A$[I,I] <= A$[J,J] THEN 190
152  REM
154  REM * IF A$(I,I) IS NOT LESS THAN A$(J,J) THEN
155  REM   WE EXCHANGE THOSE CHARACTERS
→160  LET B$=A$[I,I]
→170  LET A$[I,I]=A$[J,J]
→180  LET A$[J,J]=B$
190  NEXT J
200  NEXT I
204  REM
210  PRINT A$
220  END
RUN
ALPHA

?THE QUICK BROWN FOX JUMPS OVER THE LAZY DOG
 ABCDEEEFGHHIJKLMNOOOOPQRRSTTUUVWXYZ
```

Program REVRS simply prints the characters of a string in reverse order but keeps the string intact. Program END shows the printing of A$(I) for a sample string.

```
REVRS

94   REM * THIS PROGRAM DEMONSTRATES PRINTING THE
95   REM   CHARACTERS OF A STRING IN REVERSE ORDER
96   REM   WITHOUT MODIFYING THE CONTENTS OF
97   REM   THE STRING
100  DIM A$[72]
110  INPUT A$
120  PRINT
130  PRINT "   THE STRING CONTENTS IN REVERSE ORDER:"
134  REM
140  FOR I=LEN(A$) TO 1 STEP -1
150  PRINT A$[I,I];
160  NEXT I
164  REM
170  PRINT
180  PRINT
190  PRINT "   THE CONTENTS PRINTED IN TACT:"
200  PRINT A$
210  END
RUN
REVRS

?THIS PROGRAM PRINTS IN REVERSE

   THE STRING CONTENTS IN REVERSE ORDER:
ESREVER NI STNIRP MARGORP SIHT

   THE CONTENTS PRINTED IN TACT:
THIS PROGRAM PRINTS IN REVERSE
```

```
END

94   REM * THIS PRØGRAM DEMØNSTRATES THE USE ØF
95   REM   PRINT A$(I) IN THE SUBSTRING SCHEME
100  DIM A$[72]
110  INPUT A$
120  FØR I=LEN(A$) TØ 1 STEP -1
130  PRINT "A$(";I;") = ";A$[I]
140  NEXT I
142  REM
150  END
RUN
END

?THIS IS IT
A$( 10  ) = T
A$( 9   ) = IT
A$( 8   ) =  IT
A$( 7   ) = S IT
A$( 6   ) = IS IT
A$( 5   ) =  IS IT
A$( 4   ) = S IS IT
A$( 3   ) = IS IS IT
A$( 2   ) = HIS IS IT
A$( 1   ) = THIS IS IT
```

The ability to compare strings and substrings allows us to pack several items of information into a single string. For example, we might want to work with the days of the week. As shown in program WEEKA, we could use

110   LET A$ = "SUNMØNTUEWEDTHUFRISAT"

```
WEEKA

94    REM * THIS PRØGRAM DEMONSTRATES COMPARING A
95    REM   STRING AGAINST A SUBSTRING
→100  DIM D$[15],A$[21]
110   LET A$="SUNMØNTUEWEDTHUFRISAT"
120   INPUT D$
130   LET D=0
→140  FØR I=1 TO 19 STEP 3
150   LET D=D+1
→160  IF D$ <> A$[I,I+2] THEN 190
170   PRINT "DAY #"D
180   STOP
190   NEXT I
194   REM
200   PRINT "DAY NOT FOUND"
210   END
RUN
WEEKA

?TUE
DAY # 3
```

Then we could step through the string with

140   FØR I = 1 TØ 19 STEP 3

comparing some test string with A$(I,I+2) to see if the test string matches those three characters of A$.

We can even test parts of two strings. We could test the first three characters of D$ successively against groups of three characters in A$ looking for a match by changing line 160 to

160    IF D$(1,3) <> A$(I,I+2) THEN 190

This is left for the reader to try.

It should be clear that by the use of strings we can control what is printed in every space of the paper on our terminal. If we convert numeric values to string variables, then we gain some added flexibility for the printing of numeric results since these can be printed imbedded in strings to avoid extra spaces. If you have PRINT USING, this step is not necessary.

We shall develop here the beginnings of a routine to convert a numeric to a string. The fundamental idea is simply to pick off the digits one at a time as numbers and use the numbers to store string equivalents in the correct positions of a string variable. The way to get the string equivalent is to use what is called a dummy string. In this case the dummy string to use contains all the digits. As shown in program CØNVRT, it is D$="0123456789". The string A$ in program WEEKA is another example of a dummy string. If we want a "3" stored in the sixth position of string S$, we use the following statement:

100    LET S$(6,6) = D$(4,4)

since the "3" is really in the fourth position of D$. To get the digit "I" in the Jth position of S$, we use:

200    LET S$(J,J) = D$(I+1,I+1)

as shown in line 200 of program CØNVRT.

```
CONVRT

94    REM * THIS PROGRAM CONVERTS A NUMERIC
95    REM  TO A STRING
100   DIM S$[6],D$[10]
110   LET D$="0123456789"
120   INPUT N
130   IF N=INT(N) THEN 160
140   PRINT "INTEGERS ONLY"
150   GOTO 120
160   PRINT "*";N;"*"
170   FOR E=5 TO 0 STEP -1
180   LET J=6-E
190   LET I=INT(N/10↑E)
→ 200   LET S$[J,J]=D$[I+1,I+1]
210   LET N=N-I*10↑E
220   NEXT E
230   PRINT "$";S$;"S"
240   END
RUN
CONVRT

?975310
* 975310.    *
$975310S
```

To append a string onto the end of another string, use the technique of program CØNCAT.

```
CONCAT

94   REM * THIS PROGRAM DEMONSTRATES CONCATENATION
100  DIM AS[50],BS[50]
110  INPUT AS,BS
120  PRINT "BEFORE CONCATENATION",
130  PRINT AS,BS
140  LET AS[LEN(AS)+1]=BS
150  PRINT
160  PRINT "AFTER CONCATENATION",
170  PRINT AS,BS
180  END
RUN
CONCAT

?"CONCAT","ENATION"
BEFORE CONCATENATION            CONCAT         ENATION

AFTER CONCATENATION             CONCATENATION  ENATION
```

## Summary of Sec. 3-4

The substring scheme permits us to look at string variables in one of the following four ways:

A$          The whole string.

A$(I,J)     The substring from the Ith to the Jth characters inclusive.

A$(I,I)     The single Ith character of the string A$.

A$(I)       The substring beginning at the Ith character and continuing to the end. To obtain the beginning of the string, use A$(1,I).

We can build up new strings from parts of old ones. We can compare strings and substrings for equality and for order.

## Problems for Sec. 3-4

1) Modify ALPHA to eliminate duplicates.
2) Write a program to accept abbreviations for the days of the week and respond with the full correct spelling.
3) As written, CONVRT will print $000001$ if we input 1 for N. Eliminate these leading zeros and end up with a string only as long as needed.
4) Modify CONVRT to accept negative numbers and insert the minus sign in the string.
5) Modify CONVRT to accept decimal numbers representing dollars and cents.
6) Write a program to convert a numeric string to a true numeric stored in a numeric variable.
7) Write a program to multiply two six-digit integers and print the answer exactly.
8) Write a program like that for problem 7, but not limited to six-digit integers. (Allow 10- or 20-digit integers).
9) Write a program to encode and decode messages using a keyword.
10) Modify program WEEKA to test the first three characters of the input string from line 120 against successive sets of three characters from A$.
11) In comparing strings for order, BASIC compares the two strings one

character at a time. So for nonequal strings, the first nonequal characters determine order. Therefore when comparing such strings as '60'
and '100', BASIC will evaluate '60' as greater than '100'. Write a program to overcome this flaw. Be sure to also provide for proper ordering of strings like 'A6' and 'A10.'

## 3-5   The String Array Scheme*

Even where systems use the same general scheme, we will find differences.
Therefore we present programs here which use features found on many time-
sharing systems. Strings and string arrays may be manipulated in many of the
same ways that numerics and numeric arrays may be. That is, we may use
INPUT, READ, PRINT, assignment, and comparison for order. We generally
may not use arithmetic operations with the possible exception of addition since
some computers allow LET A$ = "ABC" + "DEF" to assign "ABCDEF" to
string variable A$. Generally speaking, we find the same dimensioning require-
ments for string arrays as for numeric arrays. So 10 DIM A$(15),B$(3,47),
C(3,8) provides for up to 16 strings in A$ (generally zero subscripts are allowed),
up to 192 strings in B$, and up to 36 numerics in C. Note that we may intermix
strings and numerics in the dimension statement. Some systems allow only one-
dimensional string arrays. The number of characters allowed in each string will
vary from system to system. The LEN( ) function, if available, evaluates the
number of characters actually stored in a string. An alternative approach uses
the CHANGE statement. CHANGE A$ T∅ A places the ASCII numeric code for
the characters in the string in the list positions of A. So if A$ = "XYZ," then
list A carries in position 1 the ASCII code for X, in position 2 the code for Y,
and in position 3 the code for Z. Moreover, A(0) will contain the number of
characters in the string A$. CHANGE also works in the other direction. Change
A T∅ A$ takes the codes stored in list A and enters the equivalent string charac-
ter in A$. With this information, we can write some sample programs.

To arrange the letters of a string in alphabetical order we may first store
the coded values in a list. We then arrange the coded values in numeric order
and convert the numeric list back to a string for printing, as shown in program
ALPHA1.

Similarly, we can reverse the order of the letters in a string with the procedure of program REVRS1. Look particularly at line 150 to see that the B list is
filled in the reverse order from the contents of the A list.

We can compare strings as a means of coding information. For instance,
we can number the days of the week by storing their names as the elements of a
list—the first day stored in the first element, the second day in the second
element, and so on. We then know which number belongs to a particular string
by which subscript we use to obtain a match, as shown in program WEEKA1.

We can compare parts of strings by proper use of the CHANGE statement
and a list for each string being compared. Program WEEKB1 looks at only the
first three letters of two strings in lines 190, 200, and 210.

---

*The programs of Sec. 3-5 were run on the General Electric Information
Services time sharing system.

ALPHA1

```
94    REM * THIS PROGRAM ORDERS THE CHARACTERS
95    REM  OF A STRING
100   DIM A(75)
110   INPUT A$
120   CHANGE A$ TO A
122
130   LET L = A(0)
140   FOR I = 1 TO L-1
150     FOR J = I+1 TO L
160         IF A(I) <= A(J) THEN 200
162
164       REM * IF OUT OF ORDER THEN EXCHANGE
170       LET X = A(I)
180       LET A(I) = A(J)
190       LET A(J) = X
200     NEXT J
210   NEXT I
212
220   CHANGE A TO A$
230   PRINT A$
240   END
RUN
ALPHA1

? THE QUICK BROWN FOX JUMPED OVER THE LAZY DOGS
      ABCDDEEEEFGHHIJKLMNOOOOPORRSTTUUVWXYZ
```

REVRS1

```
94    REM * THIS PROGRAM REVERSES THE
95    REM  CHARACTERS OF A STRING
100   DIM A(75),B(75)
110   INPUT A$
120   CHANGE A$ TO A
122
124   REM * STORE THE NUMBER OF CHARACTERS IN L AND B(0)
130   LET L = B(0) = A(0)
140   FOR I = 1 TO L
→150     LET B(L-I+1) = A(I)
160   NEXT I
162
170   CHANGE B TO A$
180   PRINT A$
190   END
RUN
REVRS1

? GOOD THINGS COME IN SMALL PACKAGES
SEGAKCAP LLAMS NI EMOC SGNIHT DOOG
```

WEEKA1

```
94    REM * THIS PROGRAM FINDS THE DAY NUMBER
95    REM  FROM THE DAY NAME
100   DIM A$(7)
110   FOR D = 1 TO 7
120     READ A$(D)
130   NEXT D
140   PRINT "DAY";
150   INPUT B$
160   FOR D = 1 TO 7
170       IF B$ <> A$(D) THEN 200
180     PRINT "DAY # "; D
190     STOP
200   NEXT D
210   PRINT B$; "NOT FOUND"
```

```
212
214   REM
220   DATA    SUNDAY, MONDAY, TUESDAY, WEDNESDAY
230   DATA    THURSDAY, FRIDAY, SATURDAY
240   END
RUN
WEEKA1

DAY? TUESDAY
DAY # 3


WEEKB1

94    REM * THIS PROGRAM DIFFERS FROM WEEKA1 BECAUSE
95    REM   IT CHECKS ONLY THE FIRST THREE CHARACTERS
96    REM   OF TWO STRINGS. SEE LINES 190 TO 210
100   DIM A$(7),A(9),B(9)
102
104   REM * READ DAYS OF THE WEEK INTO A$ LIST
110   FOR D = 1 TO 7
120      READ A$(D)
130   NEXT D
132
140   PRINT   "DAY";
150   INPUT   B$
160   CHANGE  B$ TO B
170   FOR I = 1 TO 7
180      CHANGE A$(I) TO A
182
184      REM * TEST FIRST THREE CHARACTERS
190      FOR K = 1 TO 3
200         IF A(K) <> B(K) THEN 240
210      NEXT K
220      PRINT  A$(I); " IS DAY #"; I
230      STOP
240   NEXT I
250   PRINT   B$; " NOT FOUND"
252
254   REM
260   DATA    SUNDAY, MONDAY, TUESDAY, WEDNESDAY
270   DATA    THURSDAY, FRIDAY, SATURDAY
280   END
RUN
WEEKB1

DAY? SUNDAE
SUNDAY IS DAY # 1
```

We can easily construct a program to alphabetize strings by using exactly the same approach that we use for sorting numbers except that we use subscripted string arrays instead of subscripted numeric arrays, as shown in program ∅RDER$. (For more about sorting see Sec. 11-3). Note that this program stops comparing as soon as the list is in order, an optimizing feature which obviously leads to shorter execution time.

```
ORDER$

94    REM * THIS PROGRAM ALPHABETIZES
95    REM   A LIST OF STRINGS
96    REM   THE CURRENT LIMIT IS 200 STRINGS
100   DIM L$(200)
102
104   REM * READ DATA
```

```
110   FOR I = 1 TO 200
120       READ LS(I)
130           IF LS(I) = "STOP" THEN 150
140   NEXT I
142
150   LET N = I = I-1
152
154   REM  * TURN SWITCH OFF, INCREMENT N AND SORT
160   LET S = 0
170   LET N = N -1
180   FOR J = 1 TO N
190           IF L$(J) <= L$(J+1) THEN 240
192
194       REM * EXCHANGE ELEMENTS AND TURN ON SWITCH
200       LET SS = LS(J)
210       LET LS(J) = LS(J+1)
220       LET LS(J+1) = SS
230       LET S = 1
240   NEXT J
242
244   REM * CHECK SWITCH 0=OFF, 1=ON
250       IF S = 1 THEN 160
252
254       REM * THE SWITCH IS OFF - LIST IS ORDERED
260   FOR X = 1 TO I
270       PRINT L$(X)
280   NEXT X
282
284   REM
290   DATA   WILLIAMS, JONES, SMITH
300   DATA   YOUNGMAN, STOP
310   END
RUN
ORDER$

JONES
SMITH
WILLIAMS
YOUNGMAN
```

Since strings in the scheme we are now considering may be treated as array variables, we should realize that we may MAT READ and MAT PRINT string arrays with all of the same options that these two statements allow for numerics. That is, we may MAT READ A$(M,N) to redimension the array in the MAT READ statement. And we may MAT PRINT with semicolon or comma spacing. Use semicolon spacing with care, however, as this will result in strings being printed with no spaces. For most systems, quotes are not required when placing strings in DATA statements unless the string contains a comma or is a numeral.

```
MAT$

94    REM * THIS PROGRAM DEMONSTRATES MAT READ
95    REM   AND MAT PRINT FOR STRING ARRAYS
100   DIM A$(5,10)
110   READ  R,C
120   MAT READ   A$(R,C)
130   MAT PRINT A$;
140   PRINT
150   MAT PRINT  A$,
152
154   REM
160   DATA  2,5
170   DATA  THIS, IS, A, SAMPLE, PROGRAM
180   DATA  WITH, STRING, MAT READ, AND, MAT PRINT
190   END
```

```
RUN
MAT$


THISISASAMPLEPROGRAM
WITHSTRINGMAT READANDMAT PRINT


THIS            IS              A               SAMPLE          PROGRAM

WITH            STRING          MAT READ        AND             MAT PRINT
```

Generally speaking, you need not be intimately familiar with the ASCII code because the ASC( ) function gives the numeric code for the character in parentheses. Alternatively, we may write a program to print the ASCII code for alphanumeric characters stored in a string variable, as shown in program ASC. Note that lines 130, 150, and 160 are used to store single characters from A$ in the string variable B$. Some time sharing systems provide the EXT$ function. The statement B$ = EXT$(A$,I,I) would result in the Ith character of A$ being stored in B$. Some systems use SEG$ for this. You may find numerous other functions for working with string data available in your system.

```
                    ASC

                    94    REM * THIS PROGRAM PRINTS SAMPLE
                    95    REM   ASCII CODE VALUES
                    100   DIM A(9)
                    110   LET A$ = "6 :/([ABZ"
                    120   CHANGE A$ TO A
              →  130   LET B(0) = 1
                    140   FOR X = 1 TO A(0)
              →  150      LET B(1) = A(X)
              →  160      CHANGE B TO B$
                    170      PRINT  "'"; B$; "'"; B(1)
                    180   NEXT X
                    190   END
                    RUN
                    ASC

                    '6'  54
                    ' '  32
                    ':'  58
                    '/'  47
                    '('  40
                    '['  91
                    'A'  65
                    'B'  66
                    'Z'  90
```

## Summary of Sec. 3-5

Where strings may be stored in arrays, A$(I,J) specifies a string stored in row I, column J of a string array. We may consider individual characters of the string by using CHANGE, which places equivalent numeric codes for the characters of the string in the positions of a numeric list corresponding to the position of the character in the string. In addition, the zero position of the list contains the number of characters in the string.

## Problems for Sec. 3-5

1) Modify program ALPHA1 to eliminate duplications.
2) Suppose you have typed a large quantity of data consisting of peoples names, first name first, and you suddenly find that you should have typed them last name first and in alphabetical order. Write a program to make the change. Your program should work whether or not you used middle initials.
3) Write a program to convert a string to a numeric (even though your computer may provide a function for this).
4) Write a program to accept two six-digit integers, multiply them digit by digit, and print the exact product.
5) Write a program to accept two numbers as strings not limited to six digits, find the exact product, and print it.
6) Write a program to generate license plate number and letter combinations. Establish a pattern, such as six characters with the first three alphabetic and the last three numeric. Select a few at random to print.
7) Write a program to generate 'words' where vowels and consonants alternate. Print a few at random.
8) In comparing strings for order, BASIC compares the two strings one character at a time. So for nonequal strings, the first nonequal characters determine order. Therefore, when comparing such strings as '60' and '100,' BASIC will evaluate '60' as greater then '100.' Write a program to overcome this flaw. Be sure to also provide for proper ordering of strings like 'A6' and 'A10.'

# 4
# FILES

## 4-1  Introduction

There are tremendous differences in file handling from system to system. Files give a tremendous extension of power to the BASIC language in two significant ways. First, the use of files allows us to handle far more data than we could ever store in DATA statements of a single program because of computer space limitations. Second, the use of files allows us to process the same data using several different programs. We might use one program only to enter data into a file. Another program might be used to make corrections. Another might be used to extract a particular piece of information, and yet another might be used to modify the data in the files. And so on and so on. There is no limit to the number of programs which may work on the data in a single file or group of files.

We have chosen to present here file programs on two different systems. You will want to determine which one resembles your system before attempting to write programs. The systems chosen here are Hewlett Packard and General Electric since both are in common use and differ in many ways.

## 4-2  Hewlett Packard Files

### Serial Data Files

Serial files have the advantage that they are quite efficient in the use of computer storage space. We simply print entry after entry until all desired entries are in the file or files. Serial files have the disadvantage that we cannot easily go into the file to change an existing entry or insert a new entry. To do this to a serial file, we must copy the entire contents into another file making the changes on the way and then copy the corrected data back into the original file. Naturally, this is a serious problem only if we are working with a large amount of data.

Let us construct an inventory file and work on it. Suppose that for each item of inventory we have a part name, a part number, a price, and a quantity.

Program ENTER1 will enter an initial set of inventory data into a file called INVO1.

```
ENTER1

94   REM * THIS PROGRAM ENTERS DATA IN AN EMPTY FILE
100  FILES INVO1
110  DIM P$[25]
120  READ P$,N,P,Q
130  IF N=0 THEN 240
134  REM * LINE 140 PRINTS ITEM AFTER ITEM CLOSE PACKED
135  REM  IN THE FILE MAKING IT SERIAL IN STRUCTURE
140  PRINT #1;P$,N,P,Q
150  GOTO 120
194  REM
200  DATA "FRAMIS",1001,2.3,1800,"WIDGET",1002,4.4,1100
210  DATA "REGULATOR",1003,3.48,900,"SLICNEP",1004,.04,9000
220  DATA "FRASMALATOR",1005,13.49,800,"WHATSIT",1006,10.98,3000
230  DATA "STOP",0,0,0
240  END
RUN
ENTER1


DONE
```

Line 100 is necessary to make file INVO1 available to the present program. The file must be in existence at the time the program is run. (Some HP systems provide for ASSIGNing files during program execution.) In this case, we typed the executive command ØPEN-INVO1,50 to create the file. That command specified 50 discrete storage blocks referred to as "sectors" or "records." Each of our 50 records will hold as many as 32 numerics, where one numeric occupies the same space as 4 string characters. We must add one string character each for delimiters at the beginning and end of a string and add one if the number of characters in the string is odd. The record size varies from computer to computer, and some computers allow the user to specify its length. The maximum number of records allowed varies also.

Line 120 reads from program data statements in the usual way.

Line 130 checks for dummy data.

Line 140 prints the data as read in line 120 but to the external file instead of to the paper on the terminal in front of us. The #1 is used because the file we use is the first named in the files statement. If we want to print to the second file named in a files statement, then we use PRINT #2. We can also use PRINT #F where F is the file number. File names are separated by commas in the FILES statement. For example,

100    FILES FILE1,FILE2,FILE3

makes three files available to the program in which this statement appears. Systems vary as to the number of files that may be named in a files statement. Most allow at least 8.

This is the very first time that we have run a program which failed to print anything and yet did something useful. Generally speaking, we should print something to the terminal. To prove that the data really is in that file, we present program READ to read the data out of file INVO1.

```
READ

 94   REM * READS INVENTORY DATA FROM A FILE
100   FILES INVO1
110   DIM P$[25]
120   PRINT "PART NAME","PART #","PRICE","QUANTITY"
124   REM * READ DATA FROM THE FILE
→130   READ #1;P$,N,P,Q
134   REM * PRINT THE DATA TO THE TERMINAL
140   PRINT P$,N,P,Q
150   GOTO 130
→160   END
RUN
READ
```

| PART NAME | PART # | PRICE | QUANTITY |
|---|---|---|---|
| FRAMIS | 1001 | 2.3 | 1800 |
| WIDGET | 1002 | 4.4 | 1100 |
| REGULATOR | 1003 | 3.48 | 900 |
| SLICNEP | 1004 | .04 | 9000 |
| FRASMALATOR | 1005 | 18.49 | 800 |
| WHATSIT | 1006 | 10.98 | 3000 |

```
END-OF-FILE/END OF RECORD   IN LINE 130
```

We get all of the information from the file and an error message to boot. We may avoid the error message by inserting an IF END statement. We will use 105 IF END #1 THEN 160. This statement, executed just once, sets a flag so that if line 130 tries to read nonexistent data or tries to read past the physical end of the file, the computer will next execute line 160. Alternatively, of course, we could have placed our own flag in the file by printing dummy data into the file at the end of the real data.

```
→105   IF END #1 THEN 160
RUN
READ1
```

| PART NAME | PART # | PRICE | QUANTITY |
|---|---|---|---|
| FRAMIS | 1001 | 2.3 | 1800 |
| WIDGET | 1002 | 4.4 | 1100 |
| REGULATOR | 1003 | 3.48 | 900 |
| SLICNEP | 1004 | .04 | 9000 |
| FRASMALATOR | 1005 | 18.49 | 800 |
| WHATSIT | 1006 | 10.98 | 3000 |

We can now sit down and dream up little programs to process the data in file INVO1. We might want to know the number of parts in inventory. You can easily verify that program READ2 does that.

```
READ2

 94   REM * THIS PROGRAM FINDS THE TOTAL
 95   REM NUMBER OF PARTS IN FILE INVO1
100   FILES INVO1
110   DIM P$[25]
120   LET T=0
130   IF END #1 THEN 170
140   READ #1;P$,N,P,Q
144   REM * RUNNING TOTAL CALCULATED IN LINE 150
150   LET T=T+Q
160   GOTO 140
```

```
170   PRINT T;"PARTS"
180   END
RUN
READ2

16600   PARTS
```

It is left as an exercise for the reader to find the total value of inventory with a program.

Now suppose we want to add inventory to INVO1. Using ENTER1 again with different data will simply replace what is in INVO1 with new data. (Actually, the new data might replace only part of what is already in there, and this result has other complications.) What we must do is read out to the end of the data already in the file and then begin printing new data to the file at that point, as shown in program ENTER2.

Note that program ENTER2 may also be used to enter data into an empty file. We do not need a different program for this purpose. It is a good practice to provide for printed output to the terminal in a program of this kind. We run READ1 again to make sure that the new data was properly added to the end of the file.

```
ENTER2

94    REM * THIS PROGRAM ENTERS DATA INTO AN EMPTY OR
95    REM   PARTIALLY FILLED SERIAL FILE
100   FILES INVO1
110   DIM P$[25],Q$[25]
114   REM * READ TO THE END OF EXISTING DATA
→ 120   IF  END #1 THEN 150
130   READ #1;P$,N,P,Q
140   GOTO 130
144   REM * ENTER NEW DATA INTO THE FILE
→ 150   READ P$,N,P,Q
160   IF N=0 THEN 200
170   LET Q$=P$
180   PRINT #1;P$,N,P,Q
190   GOTO 150
200   PRINT "LAST ITEM IS ";Q$
204   REM
210   DATA "LIFTER",1007,.29,10000,"DROPPER",1008,.89,1500
220   DATA "WHOSIT",1009,16,12,"HOLDER",1010,.47,1141
230   DATA "STOP",0,0,0
240   END
RUN
ENTER2

LAST ITEM IS HOLDER


RUN
READ1
```

| PART NAME | PART # | PRICE | QUANTITY |
|-----------|--------|-------|----------|
| FRAMIS | 1001 | 2.3 | 1800 |
| WIDGET | 1002 | 4.4 | 1100 |
| REGULATOR | 1003 | 3.48 | 900 |
| SLICNEP | 1004 | .04 | 9000 |
| FRASMALATOR | 1005 | 18.49 | 800 |
| WHATSIT | 1006 | 10.98 | 3000 |
| LIFTER | 1007 | .29 | 10000 |
| DROPPER | 1008 | .89 | 1500 |
| WHOSIT | 1009 | 16 | 12 |
| HOLDER | 1010 | .47 | 1141 |

The next area we might get into is that of making changes in file INVO1 according to business activity. We can do this with the procedures mentioned earlier, that is, by copying the entire contents of the file into another file, making changes on the way. However, if the amount of data becomes very great, the time lost by this method tends to be more important than the space saved by using serial files. Furthermore, there are many devices for utilizing random access files more efficiently. So let's talk about random access files.

### Random Access Files

Files are serial or random access according to the structure the programmer creates for them. In fact, the same file may be treated as serial by one program and random access by another. File INVO1 was serial because we printed the data in serially. We may instead use the discrete records of the file for specifically arranged data.

In our inventory example we might consider placing one inventory item on one record. Since most of our sample data are equivalent to about 5 numerics, this would be wasteful of computer space. However, in practice, an item of inventory will contain more data, and thus it is often wise to allow more file space than is needed at first. Then we will not have to restructure the entire storage plan as we might if we had placed several inventory items on a single record. In fact, if programmers anticipate that additional data may be required, they go one step further. They incorporate the extra variables into all programs, using zeros for numbers and empty or null strings for anticipated alphameric data. Then the existing programs will carry all of the variables needed and will not have to be rewritten to accommodate the new data structure. Of course, changes will have to be made to actually utilize the newly activated variables later. Moreover, in some situations we can use space more efficiently by storing numerics in one file and strings in another with a scheme to link the data from the two files to each other. That way numeric data may be MAT READ out of the file for very easy processing.

```
ENTER3
94   REM * THIS PRØGRAM ENTERS DATA INTØ AN EMPTY
95   REM  FILE IN RANDØM ACCESS FØRMAT
100   FILES INVO2
110   DIM P$[25]
—120   LET R=0
130   READ P$,N,P,Q
140   IF N=0 THEN 190
—150   LET R=R+1
—160   READ #1,R
—170   PRINT #1;P$,N,P,Q
180   GØTØ 130
190   PRINT R;"RECØRDS USED"
194   REM
200   DATA "FRAMIS",1001,2.3,1800,"WIDGET",1002,4.4,1100
210   DATA "REGULATØR",1003,3.48,900,"SLICNEP",1004,.04,9000
220   DATA "FRASMALATØR",1005,18.49,800,"WHATSIT",1006,10.98,3000
230   DATA "STØP",0,0,0
240   END
RUN
ENTER3

  6    RECØRDS USED
```

To keep things simple, suppose that we look at a program to place one inventory item per record, such as program ENTER3, which PRINTs inventory data into file INVO2.

Note that we have the computer print the number of records used to assure us that the program has performed as expected. Lines 120 and 150 keep track of the record to which we are going to print. Statement 160 sets a pointer in the file to the beginning of record R. Statement 170 prints data to the file beginning at the pointer. The pair of statements 160 and 170 may be replaced with the single statement, PRINT #1,R;P$,N,P,Q, the difference between the two being that if 170 attempts to print more than will fit on the record, the excess goes on the next record, whereas PRINT #1,R;P$,N,P,Q will result in an error message if the data to be printed will not fit on record R.

Now program READ1 may still be used to read the contents of INVO2 by changing line 100 to FILES INVO2.

In order to add data to the end of file INVO2, we have several techniques available to us. One is exactly analogous to that for serial files. Another uses the TYP( ) function. The TYP( ) function 'looks' at the next item of information in a file and identifies it as follows:

$$TYP(N) = 1 \qquad \text{Next item is a numeric}$$
$$TYP(N) = 2 \qquad \text{Next item is a string}$$
$$TYP(N) = 3 \qquad \text{Next item is end of file}$$
$$TYP(N) = 4 \qquad \text{Next item is end of record}$$

where N is the position that the file name occupies in the FILES statement. If N is positive, the value 4 is never returned; to detect end of record, N must be negative.

The TYP( ) function is used in line 150 of program ENTER4 to determine

```
ENTER4

94   REM * THIS PROGRAM ENTERS DATA IN A PARTIALLY FILLED
95   REM   FILE IN RANDOM ACCESS FORM
100  FILES INVO2
110  DIM P$[25]
120  LET R=0
130  LET R=R+1
140  READ #1,R
144  REM * LINE 150 DIRECTS THE COMPUTER TO LINE
145  REM   130 IF WE ARE NOT AT THE END OF DATA
150  IF TYP(1) <> 3 THEN 130
160  LET R=R-1
170  READ P$,N,P,Q
180  IF N=0 THEN 230
190  LET R=R+1
200  READ #1,R
210  PRINT #1;P$,N,P,Q
220  GOTO 170
230  PRINT R;"RECORDS USED"
234  REM
240  DATA "LIFTER",1007,.29,10000,"DROPPER",1008,.89,1500
250  DATA "WHOSIT",1009,16,12,"HOLDER",1010,.47,1141
260  DATA "STOP",0,0,0
270  END
RUN
ENTER4

10   RECORDS USED
```

the first record that has an end of file (sometimes referred to as EOF) marker and begin printing the new data on that record. Here again, as a check on the program, we have the computer tell us how many records have been used.

Now we are in a position to explore some possibilities for editing the random access file. Note that we selected part numbers, so that if we subtract 1000, we get the number of the record on which that part will be found. Often in data processing it is helpful to organize data so that something about the data tells us where to find it. This method is sometimes called "content addressing." It could consist of an extra item of data for file management purposes only.

Let's write a program that allows us to go into the inventory file and change anything but the part number. We do this with program UPDATE. The part number is requested in line 150, and the part is found in line 200. Line 210 prints the part name and offers to make a change possible. The same is done for the price in line 260 and for the quantity in line 310. When all information is correct, it is re-entered into the file in line 360. The IF END statement in line 130 provides for attempting to access a nonexistent record or for attempting to access a record that has no data on it.

```
UPDATE

    94   REM * THIS PROGRAM EDITS AN INVENTORY FILE
    100  FILES INVO2
    110  DIM P$[25],A$[3]
    120  PRINT "INPUT PART NUMBER ZERO TO QUIT"
 -> 130  IF   END #1 THEN 380
    140  PRINT
 -> 150  PRINT "PART #";
    160  INPUT N1
    170  IF N1 <> INT(N1) THEN 150
    180  IF N1=0 THEN 860
    184  REM * CALCULATE RECORD FROM PART NUMBER
    190  LET R=N1-1000
 -> 200  READ #1,R;P$,N,P,Q
    210  PRINT P$;
    220  GOSUB 800
    230  IF A$="YES" THEN 260
    240  PRINT "CHANGE TO";
    250  INPUT P$
 -> 260  PRINT "PRICE = $";P;
    270  GOSUB 800
    280  IF A$="YES" THEN 310
    290  PRINT "CHANGE TO $";
    300  INPUT P
 -> 310  PRINT "QTY =";Q;
    320  GOSUB 800
    330  IF A$="YES" THEN 360
    340  PRINT "CHANGE TO";
    350  INPUT Q
    354  REM * PRINT CORRECTED INFORMATION BACK TO THE FILE
 -> 360  PRINT #1,R;P$,N,P,Q
    370  GOTO 140
    380  PRINT "NO SUCH PART #"
    390  GOTO 140
    784  REM * YES - NO SUBROUTINE
    790  PRINT "YES OR NO"
    800  PRINT " OK";
    810  INPUT A$
    820  IF A$="YES" THEN 850
    830  IF A$="NO" THEN 850
    840  GOTO 790
    850  RETURN
    860  END
```

```
RUN
UPDATE

INPUT PART NUMBER ZERO TO QUIT

PART #?1001
FRAMIS OK?YES
PRICE = $ 2.3          OK?NO
CHANGE TO $?3.24
QTY = 1800      OK?YES

PART #?1003
REGULATOR OK?YES
PRICE = $ 3.48          OK?YES
QTY = 900    OK?NO
CHANGE TO?878

PART #?0
```

A run of READ1 confirms that the proper changes were indeed made in the file.

```
100  FILES INVO2
RUN
READ1

PART NAME       PART #        PRICE          QUANTITY
FRAMIS          1001          3.24           1800
WIDGET          1002          4.4            1100
REGULATOR       1003          3.48           878
SLICNEP         1004          .04            9000
FRASMALATOR     1005          18.49          800
WHATSIT         1006          10.98          3000
LIFTER          1007          .29            10000
DROPPER         1008          .89            1500
WHOSIT          1009          16             12
HOLDER          1010          .47            1141
```

## Summary of Sec. 4-2

We have seen that files are serial or random access depending only on the approach that a program takes in printing data to or reading data from the file. In order to treat a file as random access, the data must be placed so that its location within a record is known. Files are made available to a program with the FILES statement. We can detect the end of data or physical end of file with the IF END statement. Data is entered into a file with the PRINT # statement and read from a file with the READ # statement. In addition, we may determine the nature of the next information in the file through use of the TYP( ) function. A file pointer can be set to the beginning of record R of file F with READ #F,R without reading any data.

## Problems for Sec. 4-2

1) Arrange 10 or more strings in alphabetical order by placing them one to a record in a file.
2) Write a program to print the contents of a file without knowing the structure of the file.
3) Write a program to copy the contents of one file into another. See if you can provide for copying 'holes' too.

4) Write a program to find the first empty record and determine the number of records in the file.

## 4-3  General Electric Files

We actually are going to talk about external data files in this section, for in fact, programs are files too, and the data contained in DATA statements of a program are referred to as "internal files." The creation and use of data files can be a very complex business indeed. It is the purpose of this section to present some of the data file concepts and provide sufficient examples so that the reader will be able to use the power of files in future programming. (Our examples will of necessity handle only small amounts of data, as it would not be practical to print the entire contents of very large files.)

Files of two types are available to BASIC programs. They are called "ASCII files" and "BINARY files." ASCII files are also referred to as "Teletype files." This term reflects the fact that they may be created by typing data directly at the terminal using line numbers exactly as a program is typed at the terminal and that they may be listed directly to the terminal just as a program may be listed to the terminal. ASCII files may also be used by programs. Binary files may be used only under program control and may not be written to or read from the terminal.

### ASCII Files

Data may be typed directly to the terminal. All we have to do is create a file with the command NEW and begin typing our data as if it were a program. Each line must have a line number followed by a space followed by our data separated by commas. String and numeric data may be intermixed. Lines may be corrected by retyping them. Lines may be deleted by typing the line number followed by return. For an ASCII file to be usable at some later time, it must be saved by typing the command SAVE.

To demonstrate some of the uses of ASCII files, we have selected the names of the ten largest cities in the U.S. according to the 1960 census, their rank, and the percentage change in population from 1960 to 1970. File CITY has been created, the data typed to the terminal, and the file saved as described above. Since this is a listable file, we do so below.

```
LIST CITY
CITY

100 BALTIMORE MD,6,-4.7
110 CHICAGO ILL,2,-6.3
120 CLEVELAND OHIO,8,-15.7
130 DETROIT MICH,5,-10.6
140 HOUSTON TEXAS,7,29.3
150 LOS ANGELES CALIF,3,12.2
160 NEW YORK N.Y.,1,-.1
170 PHILADELPHIA PA.,4,-3.8
180 ST LOUIS MO,10,-19
190 WASHINGTON D.C.,9,-4.8
```

We may now write programs to access the data in file CITY. Probably the simplest useful task we could perform would be to print the contents of the file under program control.

In order to make the file available to the program we use the FILES statement in line 100 of program READCITY. We may read data from the external file in a manner similar to that with which we read data from internal files. To read from the file named in the files statement, we use READ #1 followed by the list of variables we want. This is done in line 120 of the program. Every time such a statement is executed, a pointer is moved in the file so that the next read statement begins to read at the pointer. Initially, all file pointers are at the very beginning of the file. Note that we could use READ #0 to read from the data statement of the program. Since it is possible to attempt to read past the end of the data in the file, we use the IF MØRE statement in line 140. As long as there is more data in the file, line 140 in our program will direct the computer to 120. When the data has all been read, line 140 will test false and control passes to line 150 in this case.

```
READCITY

    94    REM * THIS PRØGRAM READS THE CONTENTS OF FILE CITY
 → 100    FILES CITY
   110    PRINT "CITY"; TAB(20); "RANK"; TAB(25); "% GRØWTH"
 → 120    READ #1, C$,R,G
   130    PRINT  C$; TAB(20); R; TAB(25); G
 → 140       IF MØRE #1 THEN 120
   150    END
   RUN
   READCITY

   CITY                RANK  % GRØWTH
   BALTIMØRE MD         6     -4.7
   CHICAGØ ILL          2     -6.3
   CLEVELAND ØHIØ       8    -15.7
   DETRØIT MICH         5    -10.6
   HØUSTØN TEXAS        7     29.3
   LØS ANGELES CALIF    3     12.2
   NEW YØRK N.Y.        1     -0.1
   PHILADELPHIA PA.     4     -3.8
   ST LØUIS MØ         10     -19
   WASHINGTØN D.C.      9     -4.8
```

It turns out that ASCII files are always sequential (serial) in format. This means that data must be accessed by reading from the first set of data step by step until the desired information is obtained. There is no way to begin at some intermediate point of the file. We can, however, add data to the end of the file with an append statement. APPEND #1 sets the file pointer to the end of data in the file and prepares the file for writing. For any data processing that requires tabulating information from each line of data, the sequential nature of ASCII files is ideal. Furthermore, ASCII files are very easy to edit from the keyboard, as described earlier. Having seen how to read an ASCII file, we will next see how to write to such a file with a program.

Let's write a program to transfer the data from file CITY to file CITY1, rearranging the data so that the order in which the cities appear in the new file will be according to decreasing percentage growth. One way to create the new file is with the NEW command. Once you have named the file, type 100, press the space bar, then the return key, and save the file. Now we have to provide access to two files in one program. This is done with the FILES statement. Up to eight files may be named in a FILES statement as long as they are separated

with semicolons. These files may then be designated by number according to
the order in which they are named in the FILES statement, as shown by line 100
of program GRØWTH.

Since it is easy to sort numbers in a one-dimensional list, the strategy we
will use here is to pass through the file once, entering the percentage growth for
each city in the array A as we go. Thus A(1) becomes the percentage growth of

```
GRØWTH

94   REM * THIS PROGRAM ARRANGES TEN CITIES ACCØRDING TØ
95   REM  GRØWTH RATE USING TWØ SEQUENTIAL FILES
100  FILES CITY; CITY1
110  DIM A(10), B(10)
112
114  REM * ENTER GROWTH DATA IN ARRAY A AND ORIGINAL
115  REM  PØSITIØN IN FILE CITY IN ARRAY B
120  FØR I = 1 TØ 10
130      READ #1, N$,R,G
140      LET A(I) = G
150      LET B(I) = I
160  NEXT I
162
164  REM * BEGINNING ØF SORT
170  LET N = 10
180  LET S = 0
190  FØR I = 1 TØ N-1
200          IF A(I) >= A(I+1) THEN 280
202
204  REM * EXCHANGE ØUT ØF ORDER DATA
205  REM  AND TURN SWITCH ØN
210      LET S1 = A(I)
220      LET A(I) = A(I+1)
230      LET A(I+1) = S1
240      LET S1 = B(I)
250      LET B(I) = B(I+1)
260      LET B(I+1) = S1
270      LET S = 1
280  NEXT I
282
290  LET N = N-1
300      IF S = 1 THEN 180
302
304  REM * GRØWTH RATE IS IN ORDER NOW PRINT
305  REM  DATA IN FILE CITY1
310  SCRATCH #2
320  FØR I = 1 TØ 10
330      RESTØRE #1
340      FØR J = 1 TØ B(I)
350          READ #1, N$,R,G
360      NEXT J
362
370      WRITE #2, N$,R,G
380      PRINT N$
390  NEXT I
392
400  END
RUN
GRØWTH

HØUSTØN TEXAS
LØS ANGELES CALIF
NEW YØRK N.Y.
PHILADELPHIA PA.
BALTIMØRE MD
WASHINGTØN D.C.
CHICAGØ ILL
DETRØIT MICH
CLEVELAND ØHIØ
ST LØUIS MØ
```

the first city in the file and A(10) becomes the percentage growth of the tenth city in the file. Entering is done in lines 120 through 160. We store the original position in a B array.

Now that the list is in order we know that whatever city has the percentage growth stored in A(1) goes first in our second file and whatever city has the growth rate in A(I) goes in the Ith position of file CITY1. However, in order to prepare a file for printing, we must use the SCRATCH statement. That statement erases whatever is in a file, prepares it for write mode, and sets the file pointer at the beginning of the file. Since we want to write to the second file in our FILES statement, we use SCRATCH #2 in line 310. The next complication we face is that the pointer in file CITY is now at the end of the data. We move the pointer to the beginning of the file and keep the file in read mode with the REST∅RE statement in line 330. REST∅RE #N acts on the Nth file in the FILES statement. The REST∅RE statement must be executed every time we want to reread the file. The actual entry of the data to file CITY1 takes place in line 370 of program GR∅WTH when we have found the city with the growth rate in the Ith location of the arranged list A by reading to that city's position in the original file as determined by list B.

We now run READCITY on file CITY1 to confirm the contents of that file.

```
100   FILES CITY1
RUN
READCITY

CITY                    RANK  % GR∅WTH
H∅UST∅N TEXAS             7      29.3
L∅S ANGELES CALIF         3      12.2
NEW Y∅RK N.Y.             1      -0.1
PHILADELPHIA PA.          4      -3.8
BALTIM∅RE MD              6      -4.7
WASHINGT∅N D.C.           9      -4.8
CHICAG∅ ILL               2      -6.3
DETR∅IT MICH              5     -10.6
CLEVELAND OHIO            8     -15.7
ST L∅UIS M∅              10     -19
```

## Binary Files

Binary files are available only under program control. Whereas ASCII files may be only sequential, binary files may be either sequential or random access. Random access means that any data item may be accessed without reading all data from the beginning of the file up to that data item and that data may be written to any point in the file directly in the same manner.

An ASCII file or a binary file may be used as a sequential file as determined by the first WRITE statement which applies to that file after the file is made available for write mode by the SCRATCH statement. To work with a file as a sequential binary file simply use a colon (:) where the pound sign (#) occurs in the READ, REST∅RE, SCRATCH, IF M∅RE and WRITE statements. The distinction between ASCII and binary files, regardless of sequentiality or randomness, has to do with the code that is used to store the data on some device peripheral to the computer, and does not generally effect the programmer at the level of programming in BASIC.

## Random Access Files

Thus far we have not been concerned with how much space our data has occupied because our files simply expanded to fit whatever we had written to the file. We are not likely to exceed the maximum space available in a single file for some time. However, since random access files must have a structure allowing data to be placed in physical locations that will be known to us for future access, space requirements for data storage become important. The structure of a random access file is a little like that of a two-dimensional array except that in a file we may intermix numeric and string data. In some situations, however, we may choose to place numeric data in one file or group of files and related string data in another file or group of files, with a scheme for relating the two structures.

Random access files may be segmented into components called "records." We may assign the amount of storage space in each record at the time we create the file. Storage space is measured in computer words, and storage is required for data as follows:

1 word per numeric
1 word per 4 string characters or fraction thereof
1 word for control per string for internal computer purposes.

For example we could store 120 numerics in any file in which the product of the number of records and the number of words per record is at least 120. Since we are going to have control over the space in each record, we generally select some record size that is appropriate to our data structure, just as we usually dimension an array to fit the structure of the data we intend to store in it.

Let us begin by writing 10 random numbers to a random access file, proving that the numbers are really there and then arranging them in increasing order by using the random accessibility of the file to do the sorting.

First, the file must exist. The system command CREATE is required here. Let's provide two records which will handle 10 words each. Then our ten numbers will all fit on the first record. The executive command,

CRE RAND,(RAN(10,2))

accomplishes this. The numbers in parentheses specify the number of words per record first and the number of records second. Program RNDENTER is identical to a program that would write ten random numbers to an ASCII file except that a colon appears where a pound sign would appear in a program writing to a sequential file and no SCRATCH statement is required.

```
RNDENTER

94    REM * THIS PROGRAM WRITES 10 RANDOM NUMBERS
95    REM   TO A RANDOM ACCESS FILE
100   FILES RAND
110   RANDOMIZE
120   FOR I = 1 TO 10
130      WRITE :1, RND
140   NEXT I
142
150   END
RUN
RNDENTER
```

Note that the program generates no printed output. (It is not good general procedure to write programs with no visible output except to prove, as with program RNDENTER, that the program did in fact do something invisible.) We now need a program to read file RAND. Program RNDREAD does that.

```
RNDREAD

94    REM * THIS PROGRAM READS NUMERICS FROM A
95    REM   RANDOM ACCESS FILE SEQUENTIALLY
100   FILES RAND
110   READ :1, A
120      IF A=0 THEN 150
130   PRINT A
140   GOTO 110
150   END
RUN
RNDREAD

0.220289
0.257207
0.705748
0.717468
0.143835
0.349935
0.704994
0.649726
0.974231
0.852828
```

RNDREAD is like a program to read a sequential file, with one important difference. Look at line 120. Since we didn't put any zero values into the file, why test for zero? We would have used the IF MØRE statement in an ASCII file. IF MØRE does not determine an end of data condition in a random access file effectively because the CREATE command filled the file with binary zeros. The SCRATCH statement will have the same effect. Thus we are able to terminate our little program by reading values of A until we come up with zero. IF MØRE does determine whether or not we have reached the physical end of the file, however. Thus in our file RAND, if we had read 20 numerics, then IF MØRE :1 would test false. A companion statement IF END :1 would test true in this condition. We should be beginning to see, and will soon see even more clearly, that the total structure of the data storage is the complete responsibility of the programmer. We must know when we have reached the end of our real data. We may want to count the number of data items or we may want to place dummy data at the end of the file just as we often do for data statements of a program.

Now let us arrange the numbers of file RAND in ascending order by operating on the data within the file as we go. The basic sorting scheme is exactly like that we just used for sorting cities and that we will use again in chapter eleven. The only difference is that we are now comparing numbers that have addresses in a file instead of in a list. In order to set the file pointer to the proper location of our file, we use the SETW statement. SETW N TØ X moves the pointer in file N to the beginning of the Xth word of storage counting from the beginning of the file. This operation is totally independent of the number of words per record. Thus if a file has nine words per record, then SETW N TØ 12 moves the pointer to the beginning of the third word on the second record of

file number N.  Once the pointer is set, the next read or write statement begins
reading or writing from that point.  In our problem we will be reading a single
numeric value.

In program RNDSØRT, line 130 sets the pointer to the Ith word of the
file so that the Ith number may be read by line 140.  Line 150 sets the pointer
to the I+1st word so that the I+1st number may be read out.  If they are in the
desired order, line 170 directs the computer to line 230, which causes the next
pair of adjacent numbers to be tested.  Should the test in line 170 fail lines 180

```
RNDSORT

        94     REM * THIS PROGRAM ARRANGES 10 NUMBERS IN
        95     REM  ORDER IN A RANDOM ACCESS FILE
       100     FILES RAND
       110     LET S = 0
       120     FØR I = 1 TO 9
  --► 130          SETW 1 TO I
  --► 140          READ :1, A
  --► 150          SETW 1 TO I+1
       160          READ :1, B
  --► 170             IF A <= B THEN 230
       172
       174          REM * EXCHANGE OUT OF ORDER DATA
  ┌─ 180          SETW 1 TO I
  │    190          WRITE :1, B
--◄    200          SETW 1 TO I+1
  └─ 210          WRITE :1, A
       220          LET S = 1
  --► 230     NEXT I
       232
  --► 240          IF S = 1 THEN 110
       250     PRINT  "DØNE"
       260     END
       RUN
       RNDSØRT

       DØNE
```

through 210, exchange the positions that the two values occupied in the file.
Then a switch is turned on by setting S equal to one.  When the computer has
passed through the list, we test in line 240 to see if any exchanges have been
made.  If there have been no exchanges, then the numbers are in order and we
have the computer print "DØNE".   In the present situation, we rerun
RNDREAD to verify that the program did in fact sort the file.

```
RUN
RNDREAD

0.143835
0.220289
0.257207
0.349935
0.649726
0.704994
0.705748
0.717468
0.852828
0.974231
```

For our final example, let us take the data in the ASCII file CITY and
enter it into a random access file.  To do this we must plan very carefully, as we

must be able to specify the position of all data in the file exactly. It is usually convenient to group the data that belongs together on a single record. In our problem we have three variables: the city name, its rank, and its percentage growth. The rank and percentage growth are both numerics and so occupy one word of computer storage each. The city names are strings of different lengths and so require different amounts of space. A reasonable approach is to allow space for the largest string and dimension our file accordingly. Clearly LØS ANGELES CALIF is the longest string we use. The string has four groups of four characters and one character left over. That requires five words. We must add one word for internal control plus the two for the numerics. That puts the required space at eight words of storage per city. So we must CREATE a file with at least 10 records at eight words per record. We do this with

CRE CITY2,(RAN(8,10))

In order to set the file pointer to the beginning of the Ith record where the records contain eight words each, all we have to do is point 8(I-1)+1 words from the beginning of the file, as shown in line 140 of program XFER. This program transfers the data from ASCII file CITY to random access file CITY2. Notice that there is no difficulty whatever in accessing two different kinds of file with the same program.

```
XFER

94    REM * THIS PRØGRAM CØPIES DATA FRØM ASCII FILE CITY
95    REM   TØ RANDØM ACCESS FILE CITY2
100   FILES CITYJ CITY2
110   LET I = 0
120   READ #1, C$,R,G
130   LET I = I+1
132
134   REM * THE FØRMULA IN LINE 140 SETS THE
135   REM   PØINTER TØ THE ITH RECØRD IN THE FILE
140   SETW 2 TØ 8*(I-1)+1
150   WRITE :2, C$,R,G
160      IF MØRE #1 THEN 120
170   PRINT IJ "ENTRIES"
180   END
RUN
XFER

   10 ENTRIES
```

Our final task is to arrange the cities according to rank without using a second file and without using the technique of saving the numbers to be sorted in an array. This program, program RANK, is very similar to RNDSØRT except that the pointer is a formula and the read and write statements work with three variables instead of one.

```
RANK

94    REM * THIS PRØGRAM ØRDERS CITIES ACCØRDING TØ RANK
95    REM   IN A RANDØM ACCESS FILE
100   FILES CITY2
110   LET N1 = 0
120   LET N = 10
130   LET S = 0
140   FØR I = 1 TØ N-1
```

```
150      SETW  1  TO  8*(I-1)+1
160      READ  :1,  C$,R,G
170      SETW  1  TO  8*I+1
180      READ  :1,  C1$,R1,G1
190         IF  R  <=  R1  THEN  250
192
194      REM  *  EXCHANGE  OUT  OF  ORDER  DATA
200      SETW  1  TO  8*(I-1)+1
210      WRITE  :1,  C1$,R1,G1
220      SETW  1  TO  8*I+1
230      WRITE  :1,  C$,R,G
240      LET  S  =  1
250  NEXT  I
252
260  LET  N  =  N-1
270  LET  N1  =  N1+1
280     IF  S  =  1  THEN  130
282
290  PRINT  "CITIES  ORDERED  ON  RANK"
300  PRINT  "IN";  N1;  "PASSES"
310  END
RUN
RANK


CITIES  ORDERED  ON  RANK
IN  7  PASSES
```

Program REDCITY2 tabulates the results directly from the file.

```
REDCITY2

 94    REM  *  THIS  PROGRAM  READS  THE  CONTENTS  OF  FILE  CITY2
 95    REM     AND  PRINTS  TO  THE  TERMINAL
100    FILES  CITY2
110    PRINT  "CITY";  TAB(20);  "RANK";  TAB(25);  "% GROWTH"
120    FOR  I  =  1  TO  10
130       SETW  1  TO  8*(I-1)+1
→140       READ  :1,  C$,R,G
→150       PRINT  C$;  TAB(20);  R;  TAB(26);  G
160    NEXT  I
162
170    END
RUN
REDCITY2

CITY                    RANK  % GROWTH
NEW  YORK  N.Y.           1     -0.1
CHICAGO  ILL              2     -6.3
LOS  ANGELES  CALIF       3     12.2
PHILADELPHIA  PA.         4     -3.8
DETROIT  MICH             5    -10.6
BALTIMORE  MD             6     -4.7
HOUSTON  TEXAS            7     29.3
CLEVELAND  OHIO           8    -15.7
WASHINGTON  D.C.          9     -4.8
ST  LOUIS  MO            10     -19
```

## Summary of Sec. 4-3

ASCII and binary files are used to store and to arrange both string and numeric data. We have seen that ASCII files can be accessed either by the terminal directly or by a program, whereas binary files are available only under program control. Binary files may be either sequential or random access, but ASCII files are only sequential. In order to make any file available to a program, the

FILES statement must name the files we want, separated by semicolons. The files are numbered according to the order of appearance in the files statement. As many as eight files may be accessed by a single program simultaneously. (Provision may be made for substituting new files for previously named old ones within a program.)

The following special statements apply to ASCII files: RESTØRE #N moves the file pointer to the beginning of file N and places the file in read mode. READ #N,A,B,C$ reads values from file N for variables A,B,C$. WRITE #N,X,B$ enters the contents of X and B$ into file N. SCRATCH #N erases the contents of file N and places the file in write mode at its beginning. IF MØRE #N tests for more data in file N. IF END #N tests for the end of data condition in file N. All the above statements can be used for binary files by changing the pound sign (#) to a colon (:). There are some differences when it comes to random access files, however. SCRATCH :N, when applied to a random file, fills the file with zeros, sets the pointer to the beginning of the file, and places it in write mode. IF END and IF MØRE work only at the physical end of the file. In addition, there is a special statement for random files to place the file pointer under program control. SETW N TØ I may be used to place the file pointer of file N at the beginning of the Ith word of the file.

## Problems for Sec. 4-3

1) Enter student names followed by a fixed number of test scores in a sequential file. Arrange the students by test average and write the results to another file.

2) Suppose you have entered a large number of names in a file, last name first, one name to a string for alphabetizing. Write a program to print a list of names in alphabetical order but first name first.

3) Write a program to read numerics from two ordered files and print a single merged and ordered list to the terminal.

4) Write a program that will insert an item of data into an already ordered random access file so that the new item is in order.

5) You have a random access file with unknown contents. Write a program to determine the number of words the file contains.

6) Write a program to enter inventory data into a random access file. The data should include, for every part, a number, name, price, quantity, low order point, and reorder quantity. The low order point is the quantity that should trigger reordering for that part, and the reorder quantity is the quantity that should be ordered. Write a program or programs to do any or all of the following: modify quantity and or price according to business activity, edit the low order point and reorder quantities, process the file to find the total dollar value of the inventory, and process the file to determine what parts must be reordered and the quantities to be ordered.

# 5
# PLOTTING ON
# THE TERMINAL

## 5-1 Introduction

There are many sophisticated mechanical plotters on the market offered by a number of manufacturers. These generally use a pen which draws very short (0.01 inch is typical) straight line segments as determined by a program. The smaller the segments, the smoother the curve. However, this chapter is limited to using the terminal itself as a plotter. There are a number of disadvantages to using the terminal for this purpose. Plotting is slow and may therefore be expensive. The graphs we get are imprecise, and we can't easily use graph paper. Be all that as it may, if we have no other plotter, we can get very helpful plots from the terminal. The terminal has the advantage that it is conveniently available.

## 5-2 Plotting a Function

We can greatly simplify plotting by choosing a function, since functions have the feature that for any value of $x$ there is exactly one value for $y$. So, if we think of $y$ as increasing across the page from left to right and $x$ increasing down the page from top to bottom, when the plot is completed, we just turn the paper ninety degrees counterclockwise to obtain the conventional orientation.

To plot a single function, we first locate the origin and then concern ourselves with having the terminal mark the axes. Let's plot $y = \frac{1}{2} x + 3$. The basic plotting is very simple. All that is necessary is to use the TAB(N) printing function to get the printing mechanism out to the proper location on the paper and then print some symbol. Since the TAB function begins counting at the left margin and we would like to have negative values available for $y$ on the graph, it will be necessary to move the $x$ axis to the right. How far we move it will depend on the particular graph. We simply add some constant value to all TAB arguments. This value is set in line 110 of program GRAPH1. If your version of BASIC does not have a TAB(N) function, then you may put PRINT" "; in a loop to get the printing head to the proper spot on the paper. We print a plus sign to indicate the origin. We will therefore have to check to see if we are at $x = 0$ and then determine whether the point of the graph is to the left or the right of zero.

```
GRAPH1

94    REM * THIS IS A RUDIMENTARY PLØTTING PRØGRAM
100   DEF FNF(X) = .5*X+3
102
104   REM * K MØVES THE ØRIGIN K SPACES TØ THE RIGHT
→110  LET K = 10
120   FØR X = -7 TØ 7
130      LET Y = FNF(X)
→140     IF X <> 0 THEN 210
150      IF Y < -.5 THEN 180
152
154   REM * X = 0 AND Y >= -.5 SØ PRINT ØRIGIN
160      PRINT  TAB(K); "+";
170      IF Y < .5 THEN 220
180      PRINT  TAB( INT(Y+.5)+K ); "*";
190      IF Y < -.5 THEN 160
200      GØTØ 220
210      PRINT  TAB( INT(Y+.5)+K ); "*";
220      PRINT
230   NEXT X
232
240   END
RUN
GRAPH1
```

GRAPH1 seems to do the job we set out to do. (Be sure to turn the results ninety degrees counterclockwise to view the graph.) However, there are many improvements that we can make. Let's put in a set of axes. Since the $y$-axis is the line where $x = 0$, the $y$-axis provision can go after line 140 of GRAPH1. In order to put the $x$-axis in, we have to check for each value of $x$ whether or not the plotted point is below the $x$-axis. This is done in line 200 of GRAPH2. As long as we are working on the program, let's add a little flexibility by putting the position of the $x$-axis and the domain in as data. See lines 110, 130, and 600 of GRAPH2. Note that a distinguishing character is used to mark every tenth location in each of the axes. This greatly improves the readability of the plot. Lines 210 and 420 determine where those marks are printed.

GRAPH2

```
94      REM * THIS PROGRAM PLOTS GRAPHS OF FUNCTIONS
95      REM   WITH AXES PRINTED
100     DEF FNF(X) = .5*X+3
102
104     REM * THE VALUE OF N DETERMINES LENGTH OF Y-AXIS
105     REM   K MOVES THE GRAPH K SPACES TO THE RIGHT
106     REM   F IS THE FIRST VALUE OF X FOR THE PLOT
107     REM   L IS THE LAST VALUE OF X FOR THE PLOT
110     READ N, K, F, L
120     PRINT  TAB(K-1); "X="; F
130     FOR X = F TO L
140         LET Y = FNF(X)
150         IF X <> 0 THEN 200
152
154         REM * X = 0 SO THIS IS THE Y-AXIS
160         FOR Y1 = -K TO N-K
170             GOSUB 400
180         NEXT Y1
190         GOTO 280
192
194         REM * POINTS OFF Y-AXIS ARE PRINTED
195         REM   IN LINES 200 TO 280
200         IF Y < .5 THEN 260
210         IF X/10 <> INT(X/10) THEN 240
220     PRINT  TAB(K); "-";
230     GOTO 250
240     PRINT TAB(K); "!";
250         IF Y < .5 THEN 280
260     PRINT TAB( INT(Y+.5)+K ); "*";
270         IF Y < -.5 THEN 210
280         PRINT
290     NEXT X
292
300     PRINT  TAB(K-1); "X ="; L
310     STOP
392
394     REM * SUBROUTINE TO PRINT Y-AXIS
400         IF Y1 = 0 THEN 490
410         IF ABS(Y-Y1) < .5 THEN 470
420         IF Y1/10 = INT(Y1/10) THEN 450
430     PRINT   "-";
440     RETURN
450     PRINT   "I";
460     RETURN
470     PRINT   "*";
480     RETURN
490     PRINT   "+";
500     RETURN
502
594     REM
600     DATA  25, 10, -11, 12
610     END
```

Three runs of GRAPH2 show a variety of results. For the first RUN of GRAPH2, we present the line $y = \frac{1}{2} x + 3$ from program GRAPH1. For the second RUN, we re-define the function in line 100 to plot the parabola, $y = -.4x^2 - x + 8$. For the third RUN, we again re-define the function in line 100 to get the graph of $y = .2x^3 - 2x^2 + x + 5$.

We have in GRAPH2 a satisfactory basic graphing program, and the results may be enhanced by sketching a curve through the plotted points by hand. We can still improve on the program itself, though. Consider what the sine graph would look like using the program as it stands. The graph would show us little. Clearly we could do better by putting a scale capability in for both axes. This is left as an exercise.

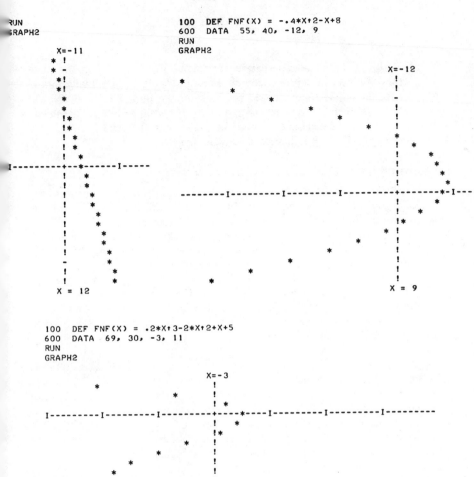

```
RUN
GRAPH2
          X=-11
          * !
          * -
          *!
          *!
          *
          *
          !*
          !*
          ! *
          !  *
          !   *
I---------+--*------I-----
          !    *
          !    *
          !    *
          !     *
          !     *
          !      *
          !      *
          !       *
          -        *
          !        *
          !         *
          X = 12
```

```
100   DEF FNF(X) = -.4*X↑2-X+8
600   DATA  55,  40,  -12,  9
RUN
GRAPH2
```

```
                                                    X=-12
   *                                                  !
              *                                       !
                 *                                    -
                        *                             !
                           *                          *
                               *                      ! *
                                                      *    *
    --------I---------I---------I-------+---------*-I---
                                               ! *
                                               ! *
                                              !*
                                         *  !
                                    *      !
                               *          !
                       *                  !
              *                           !
     *                                    !
                                          X = 9
```

```
100   DEF FNF(X) = .2*X↑3-2*X↑2+X+5
600   DATA  69,  30,  -3,  11
RUN
GRAPH2
```

```
                       X=-3
     *                  !
         *              !
                 ! *
I---------I---------I---------+----*----I---------I---------I---------
                 !    *
              *  !*
              *  !
         *      !
     *          !
         *      !
             *  !
                * !
                -        *                               *
                !
               X = 11
```

## Summary of Sec. 5-2

We have developed a program to use the terminal as a plotter. This appears to give us rough but satisfactory graphs for a variety of functions.

## Problems for Sec. 5-2

1) Modify GRAPH2 to allow a change of scale. Allow for two different scales for the two axes. Use the new program to plot any of the following:
    a) $y = \sin x$
    b) $y = \cos x$

    c) $y = x - \text{INT}(x)$

    d) $y = x + \text{INT}(x)$

    e) $y = \sqrt{x}$

2) You may have noticed that the mechanics of your terminal are such that the vertical and horizontal scales are different. On many terminals there are 10 characters per inch on the horizontal line and six lines per inch on the vertical page. Use the scaling ability of problem 1 to provide equal scale for both axes relative to the graph.

3) Modify GRAPH2 to handle more than one function.

## 5-3 Plotting Using Data Stored in an Array

There are some other things we can do with plotting. For instance, we can plot a graph that does not have to be rotated to achieve standard orientation. And we might want to plot some nonfunction relation.

One way to achieve such a capability is to set up a computer array in such a way that each storage location of the array corresponds to a coordinate point of the graph. We will have some adjustment problems, however, because for an array the "starting point" is the upper left corner and for a graph the "starting point" is generally nearer the center of things. This difficulty can be handled by shifting the "starting point" of the graph to the left and up. Also for an array, row numbers increase from top to bottom, and the reverse is true for a graph. This problem can be handled by putting the graph into the array "upside down".

We can scan through the array inserting numbers which will later be interpreted to print specific characters. Let us make the graph cover an odd number of coordinate points in each direction and make the middle element of the array correspond to the origin of the graph. We can begin by setting every entry of the array to zero, to be ignored when the printing takes place. Then we use a '1' to signify the origin, a '2' to signify the horizontal axis, a '3' to signify the vertical axis, and a '4' to signify the plotted point. This scheme will allow more relations to be handled by using numbers greater than 4 for the additional graphs.

All these features are incorporated in program GRAPH3. The axes are shifted, and the $y$-axis is turned upside down by line 230. The $y$-axis is entered in line 160. The $x$-axis is entered in line 170. The origin is entered at line 190. The use of the variable L1 is to save program storage. It takes less computer storage to set L1 equal to $L + 1$ and then use L1 (rather than $L + 1$) as long as we need this value several times, and moreover it saves typing. On some systems, storage will not be a limitation for a program like this, but if it is, then such a procedure is worth using. Line 220 tests to see if the coordinate position of the array is on the graph. This depends on our choice for the value of $t$. If the value of $t$ is .5, then we get a graph just like that of program GRAPH2. However, by increasing the value of $t$, we can have more points plotted. This tends to "fill in" the graph. Lines 110 and all other references to $D$ are employed to limit the actual use to only that part of the array that seems necessary for the graph requested. This will save printing time. As written, the program causes the printing mechanism to scan the entire line. Considerable print-

GRAPH3

```
 94   REM * GRAPH FROM DATA ENTERED IN AN ARRAY
100   DIM A(48,48)
102
104   REM * D SPECIFIES WIDTH AND HEIGHT OF GRAPH
105   REM   L IS THE NUMBER OF SPACES EACH SIDE OF ZERO
106   REM   T DETERMINES GRAPH RESOLUTION
107   REM   L1 IS USED TO SAVE TYPING L+1 REPEATEDLY
110   LET D = 21
120   LET L = (D-1)/2
130   LET T = .4
140   LET L1 = L+1
142
144   REM * ENTER AXES AND ORIGIN IN THE ARRAY
150   FOR I = 1 TO D
160      LET A(L1,I) = 3
170      LET A(I,L1) = 2
180   NEXT I
190   LET A(L1,L1) = 1
192
194   REM * NOW INSERT 4'S TO DESIGNATE PLOTTED POINTS
200   FOR Y = -L TO L
210      FOR X = -L TO L
220         IF ABS( .5*X+3-Y ) > T THEN 300
230            LET A( X+L1 , D-(Y+L) ) = 4
300      NEXT X
310   NEXT Y
312
314   REM * THE VALUES ARE STORED NOW PRINT
320   PRINT   TAB(L1); "Y"
330   FOR Y = 1 TO D
340      FOR X = 1 TO D
350         PRINT   TAB(X);
360            IF A(X,Y) = 0 THEN 380
370               GOSUB 500
380      NEXT X
390      PRINT
400   NEXT Y
410   PRINT   TAB(L); "-Y"
420   STOP
492
494   REM * PRINTING SUBROUTINE
500      IF A(X,Y) = 2 THEN 550
510      IF A(X,Y) = 3 THEN 580
520      IF A(X,Y) = 4 THEN 610
530   PRINT   "+";
540   RETURN
550      IF (X-L1)/10 = INT( (X-L1)/10 ) THEN 590
560   PRINT   "-";
570   RETURN
580      IF (Y-L1)/10 = INT( (Y-L1)/10 ) THEN 560
590   PRINT   "!";
600   RETURN
610   PRINT   "*";
620   RETURN
692
700   END
```

ing time could be saved by sending the printing head back to the beginning of the new line as soon as the last point is printed. This is left as an exercise.

Three runs of GRAPH3 are presented. The first RUN is the straight line of the first RUN of program GRAPH2; the second RUN is the parabola of the second RUN of GRAPH2; and the third RUN is a circle with radius 10 and center at the point (2,-3). Note that as with the graphs of Sec. 5-2, these graphs are distorted by the fact that the space occupied by a single character on the printed page is higher than it is wide.

RUN
GRAPH3

130  LET T = .6
220      IF ABS( -.4*X↑2-X+8-Y ) > T THEN 300
RUN
GRAPH3

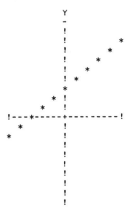

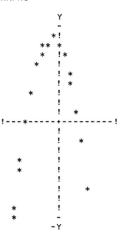

110  LET D = 29
130  LET T = 5
220      IF ABS( (X-2)↑2+(Y+3)↑2-100 ) > T THEN 300
RUN
GRAPH3

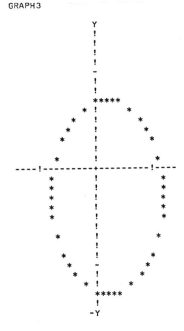

## Summary of Sec. 5-3

GRAPH3 gives us the ability to deal with many kinds of graphs fairly easily. The graph can be oriented in the conventional manner, and we can see that the ability to graph more than one relation on one set of axes is a direct extension of the current program.

## Problems for Sec. 5-3

1) Modify GRAPH3 to stop printing when the last character of the current line has been printed.

2) Modify GRAPH3 to permit two relations to be plotted. Use your program to find the approximate points of intersection of $y = 2x^2 + x - 1$ and $y = 3x + 4$.

3) Use the ideas of GRAPH3 to write your name. That is, store points to be printed in an array. If you have a long name, maybe you'd rather use the word BASIC. This exercise may be a little tedious, but fun.

4) Rewrite GRAPH3 so that the origin does not have to be the center point of the array.

5) We get an interesting effect if instead of plotting points, we plot spaces. That is, where there is no point on the graph, print an asterisk, and where there is a point, leave the location on the paper blank. Try this.

6) Modify GRAPH3 to allow different scales for the two axes. Then plot a large circle to see how well you can do.

7) On some systems, the array size allowed is limited enough to make some plots not practical if we use the methods of this section. One way to program around this is to notice that there is a tremendous amount of wasted storage in each element of the array itself. Note that for up to six relations GRAPH3 requires only a one digit number to store the information required for graphing. Since most computers provide at least six digits, by using each of those digits we can increase the storage by a factor of six. Write a graphing program to use this additional storage space.

8) One method for obtaining larger graphs is described in problem 7. Another procedure would be simply to analyze the graph one line at a time. Try this.

# 6
# AREA UNDER
# A CURVE

## 6-1  Introduction

Let us consider a moving object.  At constant speed, the distance traveled is simply its speed multiplied by time.  If an object travels 15 feet per second for 5 seconds, it will travel 75 feet.  However, it is often true that the speed of an object is not constant.  Suppose the graph of Fig. 6-1 represents an object in nonconstant motion.  The distance the object has traveled at time t is the area under the graph from the origin to t.  For Fig. 6-1 that area is a convenient geometric shape.  We get Area = A = $\frac{1}{2}$*60*3 = 90 ft.

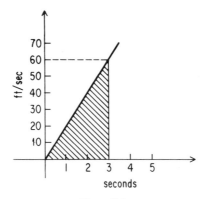

**Figure 6-1**

Now suppose a graph does not provide such a convenient geometric shape, as in Fig. 6-2.

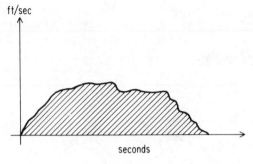

ft/sec

seconds

**Figure 6-2**

To find the total area of such a shape, we can subdivide the area into many smaller segments, find the area of each segment, and sum up the individual areas. All we have to do is decide what kind of smaller segments to use and how large they should be. Consider Fig. 6-3.

**Figure 6-3**

Figure 6-3 subdivides the area into rectangles so constructed that each one falls completely within the desired area. Thus we know that the sum of these areas will be less than the actual area. We could alternatively place the rectangles as shown in Fig. 6-4. But that would have the opposite effect on the accuracy. Another possibility is to construct the rectangles so that the midpoint of the top

**Figure 6-4**

side is a point of the curve, as shown in Fig. 6-5. Now we have some area included by the rectangles that is not included by the actual curve and some area included by the curve but excluded by the rectangles. Thus we expect some cancelling-out effect.

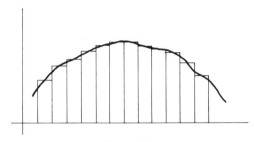

**Figure 6-5**

Let us begin by writing a program to sum up the area shown in Fig. 6-5. In order to test the program, we can make our first function contain a known area. We choose a semicircle derived from the circle $(x - 5)^2 + y^2 = 25$. This circle has a radius of 5 and its center at the point (5,0), as shown in Fig. 6-6A, and so the area we expect is $\frac{1}{2} \pi r^2$ or $(\pi * 5^2)/2$.

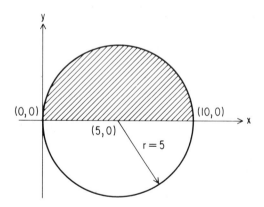

**Figure 6-6A**

The curve we are considering is in fact a function from 0 to 10 for $x$. Solving $(x - 5)^2 + y^2 = 25$ for $y^2$, we get

$$y^2 = 25 - (x - 5)^2$$

and

$$y = \sqrt{25 - (x - 5)^2}$$

For the shaded area of Fig. 6-6A, the function is

$$y = f(x) = \sqrt{25 - (x - 5)^2}$$

Thus we can easily define a computer function as follows:

$$100 \quad DEF \ FNS(X) = SQR(25 - (X-5)\uparrow 2))$$

For this problem we can begin by taking 10 intervals one unit wide. Then the midpoint of an interval will be $x - .5$, and the height of the rectangle will be $FNS(X - .5)$. See Fig. 6-6B and program AREA1.

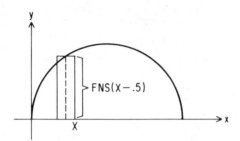

**Figure 6-6B**

AREA1

```
94    REM * THIS PRØGRAM CØMPARES THE AREA ØF A
95    REM   SEMICIRCLE FØUND BY FØRMULA AND BY
96    REM   SUMMING AREAS ØF RECTANGLES.
100   DEF FNS(X) = SQR( 25-(X-5)↑2 )
110   LET A = 3.14159*25*.5
120   PRINT  "AREA ØF SEMICIRCLE BY FØRMULA ="; A
130   LET A = 0
132
134   REM * THE LENGTH ØF THE BASE IS B
140   LET B = 1
150   FØR X = 1 TØ 10
152
154      REM * THE HEIGHT IS H
160      LET H = FNS(X-.5)
162
164      REM * THE AREA ØF CURRENT RECTANGLE IS B*H
170      LET A = A + B*H
180   NEXT X
182
190   PRINT  TAB(3); "AREA BY SUMMING RECTANGLES ="; A
200   END
RUN
AREA1

AREA ØF SEMICIRCLE BY FØRMULA = 39.2699
    AREA BY SUMMING RECTANGLES = 39.6499
```

The relative error is about .38 in 39 or about 1%. We can improve on this by taking smaller intervals within the accuracy of the computer.

Let's rewrite program AREA1 to allow varying widths of intervals. We can take the $b = 1$ out of the $x$ loop and allow the value of $b$ to be read from data.

Now since the width of interval will change according to the value of $b$, the midpoint of the interval will be $x - b/2$, and the value of $x$ must be successively incremented by $b$, the interval width. While we are at it, let us allow the value of $x$ to have a variable range read as data. This is done in lines 140 and 160 of AREA2.

```
AREA2

94    REM * THIS PRØGRAM SUMS RECTANGLES TØ
95    REM   APPRØXIMATE AN AREA ALLØWING THE
96    REM   WIDTH ØF THE RECTANGLES TØ BE READ
97    REM   AS DATA.
100   DEF FNS(X) = SQR( 25-(X-5)↑2 )
110   PRINT  "FRØM",  "INTERVAL",  "TØ",  "AREA"
120   READ B
130      IF B = 0 THEN 250
140   READ F,T
150   LET A = 0
160   FØR X = F+B TØ T STEP B
170      LET H = FNS( X-B/2 )
180      LET A = A + B*H
190   NEXT X
192
200   PRINT F, B, T, A
210   GØTØ 120
212
214   REM
220   DATA  1,0,10,    .5,0,10
230   DATA  .1,0,10,   .01,0,10
240   DATA  0
250   END
RUN
AREA2

FRØM            INTERVAL            TØ            AREA
0               1                   10            39.6499
0               .5                  10            39.4051
0               .1                  10            39.2115
0               .01                 10            39.2674
```

The results of AREA2 do indeed give successively more accurate approximations of the area.

Now we run AREA2 for the function,

$$f(x) = 2x^3 - 2x^2 + x + 5$$

from $-3$ to 11 for $x$. For a graph of this function, see Sec. 5-2.

```
100   DEF FNS(X) = 2*X↑3 - 2*X↑2 + X + 5
220   DATA  1,-3,11,    .5,-3,11
230   DATA  .05,-3,11
RUN
AREA2

FRØM            INTERVAL            TØ            AREA
-3              1                   11            6475
-3              .5                  11            6494.25
-3              .05                 11            6500.62
```

## Summary of Chapter 6

We have developed a routine that approximates the area under a curve for functions. The method used is to sum up areas of rectangles whose heights are determined by the midpoint of the intervals. (There are several other methods, which are left as exercises.)

## Problems for Chapter 6

1) Find the area enclosed by $y = x + 3$ and $y = x^2 - 8x + 17$.
2) Find the area enclosed by $y = -3x^2 + 4x + 2$ and the line $y = -3$.
3) Another procedure for finding area under a curve is called the trapezoid method. This is done by inscribing trapezoids instead of rectangles under the curve. Write a program to use the trapezoid method.
4) Write a program that begins with a specified width and automatically makes the subdivisions smaller until the new approximation does not differ from the old approximation by more than some percentage error, say .01%.
5) Write a program to approximate area by making the first interval the whole domain and each subsequent interval one half the previous interval. Have the computer stop when the percentage change is less than, say, .01%.
6) A method always as accurate and usually more accurate than the trapezoid method is Simpson's rule. Simpson's rule requires an even number of intervals and is given by the following (see Fig. 6-7):

$$A = \frac{W}{3}(f_1 + 4f_2 + 2f_3 + 4f_4 + \cdots + 2f_{n-2} + 4f_{n-1} + f_n)$$

Write a program to use Simpson's rule.

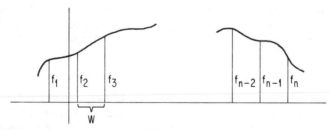

Figure 6-7

7) Use the ideas of this section to find the length of the graphed line of a continuous function instead of the area.

# 7
# COORDINATE
# GEOMETRY

## 7-1  Points in a Plane

In the Cartesian coordinate system, points in a plane are named by ordered pairs of real numbers. A point is labeled $p(x, y)$, where the first number is called the $x$-coordinate and the second is called the $y$-coordinate. As we consider the ordered pairs of numbers associated with a point or set of points, many geometric relationships unfold. For two points in a plane, we can look at the distance between them or consider the straight line they determine. For three points in a plane, we may be interested in whether or not they fall on a straight line, that is, are collinear. If not collinear, then three points determine a triangle which has many properties of interest. We may examine many other common geometric figures such as quadrilaterals, circles, parabolas, etc. It is the purpose of this chapter to study some of these topics, using the computer to assist us.

## 7-2  Pairs of Points

Consider the two points A(3,5) and B(3, -1), as shown in Fig. 7-1. Clearly the distance AB from A to B is six units, usually stated simply as 6. We define the distance between two points with the same $x$-coordinate as the absolute value of the difference in $y$-coordinates. (For two points with the same $y$-coordinate, the distance is defined as the absolute value of the difference in $x$-coordinates.) Thus in Fig. 7-1,

$$AB = |5 - (-1)| = |5 + 1| = 6.$$

Left only with this definition we would have a very limited ability to determine distance. We should, however, be interested in determining distance for any two points whatever their coordinates.

**Figure 7-1**

For the points A(3,5) and B(-1,2), we may find the distance by plotting the points and constructing a right triangle, as shown in Fig. 7-2.

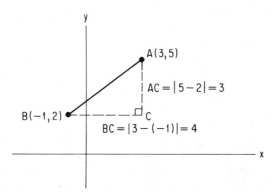

**Figure 7-2**

Using the Pythagorean Theorem,

$$AB^2 = BC^2 + AC^2$$

or

$$AB = \sqrt{BC^2 + AC^2}$$

so that

$$AB = \sqrt{4^2 + 3^2}$$

$$AB = \sqrt{25}$$

$$AB = 5$$

It is evident that for any two points $A(x_1, y_1)$ and $B(x_2, y_2)$ we have the relationships shown in Fig. 7-3.

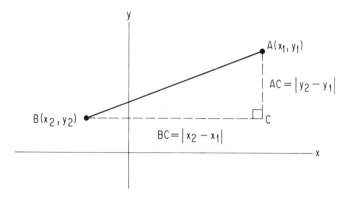

**Figure 7-3**

Using $AB = \sqrt{BC^2 + AC^2}$, we get

$$AB = \sqrt{|x_2 - x_1|^2 + |y_2 - y_1|^2}$$

but since the square of a number equals the square of its absolute value, we get

$$AB = \sqrt{(x_2 - x_1)^2 + (y_2 - y_1)^2}$$

This is known as the distance formula.

We shall now find distances for pairs of points. The distance formula translates readily into the BASIC statement:

200   LET D = SQR ( (X2 - X1) ↑2) + (Y2 - Y1) ↑2 )

All that remains is to get coordinate pairs read into the computer and results printed out. This is done in program DIST1.

```
DIST1

 94    REM * THIS PRØGRAM FINDS THE DISTANCE AB
 95    REM   FØR THE CØØRDINATES (X1,Y1) AND (X2,Y2)
100    PRINT   "TØ FIND THE DISTANCE BETWEEN TWØ PØINTS"
150    PRINT
160    PRINT   "PØINT A";
170    INPUT   X1,Y1
180    PRINT   "PØINT B";
190    INPUT   X2,Y2
192
194    REM * CALCULATE DISTANCE AND PRINT IT
200    LET D = SQR( (X2-X1)↑2 + (Y2-Y1)↑2 )
210    PRINT   "DISTANCE AB ="; D
222
230    END
RUN
DIST1

TØ FIND THE DISTANCE BETWEEN TWØ PØINTS

PØINT A?3,5
PØINT B?-1,2
DISTANCE AB = 5
```

Program DIST1 works fine for a single pair of points. But suppose we had several pairs of points. We may simply request the number of calculations desired and use FØR-NEXT, as shown in DIST2.

```
DIST2

 94    REM * FINDS DISTANCE FØR PAIRS ØF PØINTS
 95    REM  PERMITS MØRE THAN ØNE SET ØF DATA
100    PRINT   "TØ FIND THE DISTANCE BETWEEN TWØ PØINTS"
110    PRINT
120    PRINT   "NØW MANY PAIRS"J
130    INPUT N
132
140    FØR I = 1 TØ N
150       PRINT
160       PRINT   "PØINT A"J
170       INPUT   X1,Y1
180       PRINT   "PØINT B"J
190       INPUT   X2,Y2
192
194       REM * CALCULATE DISTANCE AND PRINT IT
200       LET D = SQR( (X2-X1)+2 + (Y2-Y1)+2 )
210       PRINT   "DISTANCE AB ="J D
220    NEXT I
222
230    END
RUN
DIST2

TØ FIND THE DISTANCE BETWEEN TWØ PØINTS

NØW MANY PAIRS?2

PØINT A?3,4
PØINT B?0,0
DISTANCE AB = 5

PØINT A?-3.4, 5.75
PØINT B?3.125, 2
DISTANCE AB = 7.52583
```

For any two points A and B, it can be shown that the coordinates of the midpoint of segment AB are found by taking the average of the corresponding coordinates of A and B. Thus the midpoint of AB for $A(x_1,y_1)$ and $B(x_2,y_2)$ is

$$\frac{x_1 + x_2}{2} , \frac{y_1 + y_2}{2}$$

It is left as an exercise for the reader to write a program to give coordinates of midpoints.

Where coordinates of two points are known, another property of interest is the slope of the line they determine. The slope is the ratio of the change in $y$-coordinates to the change in $x$-coordinates, or

$$\text{Slope} = m = \frac{y_2 - y_1}{x_2 - x_1}$$

Thus for A(1,3) and B(5,6),

$$m = \frac{6 - 3}{5 - 1} = \frac{3}{4}$$

and for $A(3, -4)$ and $B(1, 6)$,

$$m = \frac{6 - (-4)}{1 - 3} = \frac{10}{-2} = -5$$

Note that slopes up and to the right are positive and slopes up and to the left are negative. A short program can easily be written to make the above calculation, as shown by program SLØPE.

```
SLØPE

100   PRINT   "THIS PRØGRAM FINDS THE SLØPE ØF AB"
110   PRINT
120   PRINT   "HØW MANY PRØBLEMS";
130   INPUT   N
140   FØR I = 1 TØ N
142
150      PRINT
160      PRINT   "PØINT A";
170      INPUT   X1,Y1
180      PRINT   "PØINT B";
190      INPUT   X2,Y2
192
194   REM * CALCULATE SLØPE AND PRINT IT
230      LET M = (Y2-Y1)/(X2-X1)
240      PRINT   "SLØPE =";  M
250   NEXT I
252
260   END
RUN
SLØPE

THIS PRØGRAM FINDS THE SLØPE ØF AB

HØW MANY PRØBLEMS?2

PØINT A?0,0
PØINT B?4,5
SLØPE = 1.25

PØINT A?3,6
PØINT B?5,-3
SLØPE =-4.5
```

Look at line 230 in program SLØPE. Note that we instruct the computer to perform division. When two points have the same $x$-coordinate, division by zero is required, which is a mathematically, and thus computationally, undefined condition. The program should be modified to test the value of $x_2 - x_1$ before allowing division to take place. This is left as an exercise for the reader.

The idea that two points determine a line has been referred to several times. It can be shown that any line in a plane can be described by an equation of the form $ax + by + c = 0$, where $a$, $b$, and $c$ are constants. This is called the general form of the equation. It can also be shown that all nonvertical lines can be described by an equation of the form $y = mx + k$, where $m$ is the slope as defined earlier and $k$ is the value of $y$ when $x = 0$, that is, the value of $y$

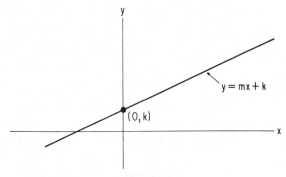

**Figure 7-4**

where the line crosses the $y$-axis, called the $y$-intercept, as shown in Fig. 7-4. The form $y = mx + k$ is called the slope-intercept form.

If we are given two points, we can find $m$ in $y = mx + k$. Then we can get a value for $k$ by solving $y = mx + k$ for $k$ to get $k = y - mx$. With a value for $m$ and a value for $k$, we can write the equation of the line in slope-intercept form by using program LINE1.

```
LINE 1
94    REM * THIS PRØGRAM PRØDUCES THE EQUATIØN ØF A LINE
95    REM   IN SLØPE-INTERCEPT FØRM GIVEN CØØRDINATES FØR
96    REM   TWØ PØINTS ØN THE LINE. THE PRØGRAM USES X =
97    REM   A CØNSTANT FØR VERTICAL LINES
100   PRINT  "EQUATIØN ØF A STRAIGHT LINE IN"
110   PRINT  "SLØPE-INTERCEPT FØRM GIVEN TWØ PØINTS"
120   READ X1,Y1, X2,Y2
130      IF X1 = .001 THEN 250
140   PRINT
150   PRINT  "(";  X1; ","; Y1; "),(";  X2; ","; Y2; ")"
152
154   REM * TEST FØR DEFINED SLØPE
160      IF X2-X1 <> 0 THEN 190
170   PRINT  "EQUATIØN IS: X =";  X1
180   GØTØ 120
182
184   REM * CALCULATE SLØPE AND INTERCEPT
185   REM   THEN PRINT SØLUTIØN EQUATIØN
190   LET M = (Y2-Y1)/(X2-X1)
200   LET K = Y1 - M*X1
210   PRINT  "EQUATIØN IS: Y =";  M;  "*X+(";  K;  ")"
220   GØTØ 120
222
224   REM
230   DATA  3,4, 5,6,  -1,6,  -1,3
240   DATA  .001,0,  0,0
250   END
RUN
LINE 1

EQUATIØN ØF A STRAIGHT LINE IN
SLØPE-INTERCEPT FØRM GIVEN TWØ PØINTS

( 3    , 4    ),( 5    , 6    )
EQUATIØN IS: Y = 1     *X+( 1    )

(-1    , 6    ),(-1    , 3    )
EQUATIØN IS: X =-1
```

## Summary of Sec. 7-2

For two points we have found the coordinates of the midpoint of the segment they determine. We have found the distance, the slope, and the equation of the line in slope-intercept form.

## Problems for Sec. 7-2

1) Modify program SLØPE to accommodate data for which the slope is undefined.
2) Write a program to calculate the coordinates of the midpoint for pairs of points.
3) Modify program LINE1 to treat a horizontal line as a special case.
4) Modify program DIST1 or DIST2 to give the distance in simplified radical form.
5) Modify LINE1 to give the slope as a decimal, integer, or fraction reduced to lowest terms as appropriate.
6) For an equation in slope-intercept form, have the computer give a table of $(x,y)$ values suitable for graphing.
7) For an equation in general form, have the computer give a table of $(x,y)$ values suitable for graphing.
8) For a set of $n$ points, write a program to give equations for all possible pairs of points. Enter the $n$ points as DATA and store them in a 2 by $n$ array or in a pair of lists.
9) For problem 8, have the computer eliminate duplicate points and therefore duplicate lines in the output.
10) Write a program to write the equation of a line, given two points, in $ax + by + c = 0$ form. Treat vertical and horizontal lines as special cases.
11) Modify program LINE1 to find the slope and $y$-intercept as fractions reduced to lowest terms, if appropriate.

## 7-3 Parallel and Perpendicular Lines

What happens when we begin to think about more than one line in a plane? Lines either intersect or they don't. If they don't, then the lines are parallel, in which case their slopes are equal unless the lines are vertical, making both the slopes undefined. If the lines intersect, then they might be perpendicular. What about the situation for perpendicular lines? Consider Fig. 7-5.

Note that the slope of $l_1$ is positive and the slope of $l_2$ is negative. Thus,

$$m_1 = \frac{d_1}{t} \tag{7-1}$$

and

$$m_2 = -\frac{d_2}{t} \tag{7-2}$$

Since $l_1$ and $l_2$ are perpendicular, right triangles ABC and AB'C are similar and

$$\frac{d_1}{t} = \frac{t}{d_2} \tag{7-3}$$

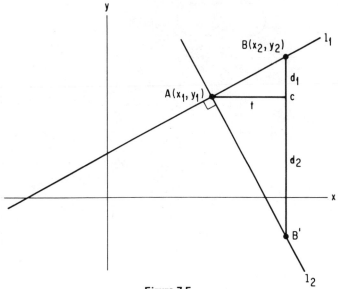

**Figure 7-5**

because ratios of lengths of corresponding sides of similar triangles are equal. Since

$$m_2 = -\frac{d_2}{t} \tag{7-4}$$

we get

$$\frac{t}{d_2} = -\frac{1}{m_2} \tag{7-5}$$

Substituting from (7-1) and (7-5) above into (7-3), we get

$$m_1 = -\frac{1}{m_2} \tag{7-6}$$

which gives

$$m_1 m_2 = -1 \tag{7-7}$$

That is, for perpendicular lines having slopes $m_1$ and $m_2$, the product of the slopes is $-1$, or the slopes are negative reciprocals of each other.

We can use the parallel and perpendicular properties for a variety of problems. We can test lines to see if they are either parallel or perpendicular. We can find the equation of a line through a fixed point parallel or perpendicular to another line. We can write the equation of a line which is the perpendicular bisector of a segment.

We shall now present a program to give an equation for the line through a given point perpendicular to the line determined by a pair of given points. There are many conditions that we must account for. Suppose the given points determine a vertical or a horizontal line? We might even be given the same point

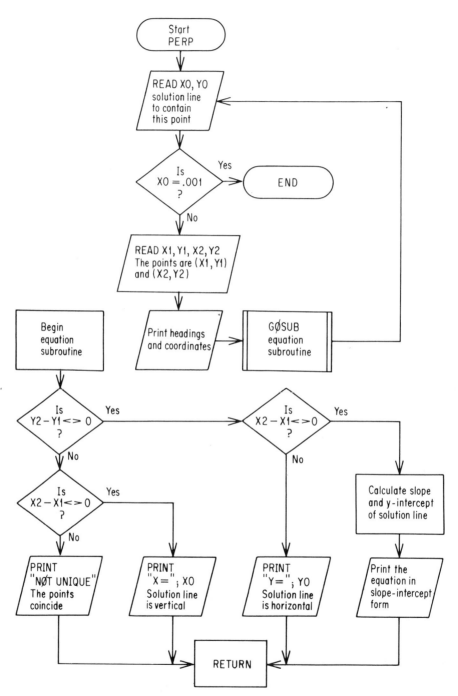

**Figure 7-6** Flowchart for finding the equation of a line given one point on the line and two points determining a line perpendicular to it.

twice. A flowchart should be helpful in organizing these conditions. See Fig. 7-6 and program PERP.

```
PERP

94    REM * THIS PRØGRAM ATTEMPTS TØ WRITE AN EQUATIØN
95    REM   FØR A STRAIGHT LINE CØNTAINING THE GIVEN PØINT
96    REM   (XO,YO) AND PERPENDICULAR TØ THE LINE
97    REM   DETERMINED BY THE GIVEN PØINTS (X1,Y1)
98    REM   AND (X2,Y2).
100   READ XO,YO
110      IF XO = .001 THEN 800
120   READ X1,Y1, X2,Y2
130   PRINT
140   PRINT  "LINE THRØUGH ("; XO; ","; YO; ")"
150   PRINT  "PERPENDICULAR TØ THE LINE THRØUGH PØINTS"
160   PRINT  "("; X1; ","; Y1; "),("; X2; ","; Y2; ")"
170   PRINT  "  EQUATIØN IS: ";
180   GØSUB 500
190   GØTØ 100
492
494   REM * SUBRØUTINE TØ DETERMINE AND PRINT EQUATIØN
500   LET V = Y2-Y1
510   LET H = X2-X1
520      IF V <> 0 THEN 560
530      IF H <> 0 THEN 590
532
534   REM * THE TWØ GIVEN PØINTS CØINCIDE
540   PRINT  "NØT UNIQUE"
550   RETURN
560      IF H <> 0 THEN 610
562
564   REM * SØLUTIØN LINE IS HØRIZØNTAL
570   PRINT  "Y ="; YO
580   RETURN
582
584   REM * SØLUTIØN LINE IS VERTICAL
590   PRINT  "X ="; XO
600   RETURN
602
604   REM * DEFINED NØN-ZERØ SLØPE
610   LET M = V/H
620   LET MO = -1/M
630   LET K = YO - MO*XO
640   PRINT  "Y ="; MO; "*X+("; K; ")"
650   RETURN
652
704   REM
710   DATA  1,2,   4,7,4,7,   4,3,   -1,9,4,5
720   DATA  5,-2,  6,4,6,-8,  3,8,   18,5,-11,5
730   DATA  .001,0
800   END


RUN
PERP


LINE THRØUGH ( 1    , 2    )
PERPENDICULAR TØ THE LINE THRØUGH PØINTS
( 4    , 7    ),( 4    , 7    )
    EQUATIØN IS: NØT UNIQUE

LINE THRØUGH ( 4    , 3    )
PERPENDICULAR TØ THE LINE THRØUGH PØINTS
(-1    , 9    ),( 4    , 5    )
    EQUATIØN IS: Y = 1.25      *X+(-2    )

LINE THRØUGH ( 5    ,-2    )
PERPENDICULAR TØ THE LINE THRØUGH PØINTS
( 6    , 4    ),( 6    ,-8    )
    EQUATIØN IS: Y =-2
```

```
LINE THROUGH ( 3      , 8     )
PERPENDICULAR TO THE LINE THROUGH POINTS
( 18   , 5    ),(-11   , 5    )
    EQUATION IS: X = 3
```

## Summary of Sec. 7-3

We have examined pairs of lines in a plane. If they are parallel and non-vertical, their slopes are equal. If two lines are perpendicular and neither is vertical, the product of their slopes is $-1$.

## Problems for Sec. 7-3

1) Change program PERP to write the equation of the new line parallel to the line determined by the given pair of points.
2) Write a program to give the equation of the perpendicular bisector of a segment, given its endpoints.
3) For two pairs of points entered as DATA, have the computer determine if the specified lines are parallel or perpendicular. Be sure to permit vertical lines.
4) For two lines given in $ax + by + c = 0$ form, have the computer determine whether the lines are parallel, perpendicular, or neither.

## 7-4  Point of Intersection of Two Lines

We can define two lines to work with in several ways. One is to give a pair of points to define each line. Another is to give an equation in the form $y = mx + k$ by specifying $m$ and $k$ for each line. Yet another is to give equations in the form $ax + by + c = 0$ by specifying $(a,b,c)$ for each line. We may become more familiar with the general form by working with data for equations in the form $(a,b,c)$.

Given two lines,

$$a_1 x + b_1 y + c_1 = 0 \qquad (7\text{-}8)$$

and

$$a_2 x + b_2 y + c_2 = 0 \qquad (7\text{-}9)$$

and the need to find the point of intersection, we must find a coordinate pair $(x,y)$ that fits both equations. That is, we have to solve the equations simultaneously. Since the computer does not "do algebra," we will have to.

Rearranging the above equations, we get

$$a_1 x + b_1 y = -c_1 \qquad (7\text{-}10)$$

$$a_2 x + b_2 y = -c_2 \qquad (7\text{-}11)$$

Multiplying Eq. (7-10) through by $-a_2$ and Eq. (7-11) by $a_1$ gives

$$-a_2 a_1 x - a_2 b_1 y = a_2 c_1 \qquad (7\text{-}12)$$

$$a_2 a_1 x + a_1 b_2 y = -a_1 c_2 \qquad (7\text{-}13)$$

Adding Eqs. (7-12) and (7-13) produces

$$a_1 b_2 y - a_2 b_1 y = a_2 c_1 - a_1 c_2 \qquad (7\text{-}14)$$

Factoring, we get

$$y(a_1 b_2 - a_2 b_1) = a_2 c_1 - a_1 c_2 \qquad (7\text{-}15)$$

Dividing both sides by $a_1 b_2 - a_2 b_1$ leaves

$$y = \frac{a_2 c_1 - a_1 c_2}{a_1 b_2 - a_2 b_1} \qquad (7\text{-}16)$$

Following a similar procedure to solve for x, we get

$$x = \frac{b_1 c_2 - b_2 c_1}{b_2 a_1 - b_1 a_2} \qquad (7\text{-}17)$$

Let's write a program to use the above results to find the point of intersection, if it exists. Note that in Eqs. (7-16) and (7-17) the denominators are equal. So we may use the BASIC statement,

$$180 \quad \text{LET D } = \text{A1*B2 } - \text{ A2*B1}$$

This will allow us to divide the numerators from Eqs. (7-16) and (7-17) by D to obtain the values for $y$ and $x$, respectively, unless D happens to equal zero. This situation would require division by zero, which means that the value is either indeterminant or undefined depending on whether the numerator is zero or not. Thus, if the value of D is not zero, we have a unique intersection, which we may calculate using Eqs. (7-16) and (7-17). If D equals zero, we may obtain more information about the two lines as outlined in the following discussion.

D = 0 means the following:

$$a_1 b_2 - a_2 b_1 = 0 \qquad (7\text{-}18)$$

and therefore

$$a_1 b_2 = a_2 b_1 \qquad (7\text{-}19)$$

which may be written

$$\frac{a_1}{b_1} = \frac{a_2}{b_2} \qquad (7\text{-}20)$$

To see the significance of this, let's look at the original equations, (7-8) and (7-9). They are $a_1 x + b_1 y + c_1 = 0$ and $a_2 x + b_2 y + c_2 = 0$. Solving each for $y$ we get:

$$y = -\frac{a_1 x}{b_1} - \frac{c_1}{b_1} \qquad (7\text{-}21)$$

and

$$y = -\frac{a_2 x}{b_2} - \frac{c_2}{b_2} \qquad (7\text{-}22)$$

Now the equations are in $y = mx + k$ form. Notice that the slope of line 1 in Eq. (7-21) is $-a_1/b_1$ and of line 2 in Eq (7-22) is $-a_2/b_2$ unless $b_1$ or $b_2$ is zero. Clearly by multiplying both sides of Eq. (7-20) by $-1$ we get

$$-\frac{a_1}{b_1} = -\frac{a_2}{b_2} \qquad (7\text{-}23)$$

Since the two sides of Eq. (7-23) are the slopes of the lines in Eqs. (7-21) and (7-22), that makes line 1 parallel to line 2. To sum up, if D = 0, then the lines are parallel and there is no solution unless $b_1$ or $b_2$ is zero.

Now suppose that either $b_1$ or $b_2$ is zero when D = 0. Looking at Eq. (7-19), if $b_1 = 0$ then either $a_1$ or $b_2$ is also zero. Now, if Eq. (7-8) is not meaningless, that means that $b_2$ must also be zero. If $b_1$ and $b_2$ are both zero, we get

$$a_1 x + c_1 = 0 \text{ or } x = -\frac{c_1}{a_1} \qquad (7\text{-}24)$$

$$a_2 x + c_2 = 0 \text{ or } x = -\frac{c_2}{a_2} \qquad (7\text{-}25)$$

in which case both lines are vertical because $x$ is constant. If what we are looking for is the point of intersection, there won't be any unless the two equations define the same line, in which case all points on one line will also lie on the other.

We really have three levels of information to test for. First we want to know if the lines intersect in a single point. If they do intersect in a single point, then we want the coordinates of that point. If they don't intersect in a single point, then it is useful to know whether or not they are vertical, because if one is, they both are. And finally, we can determine whether or not they coincide. If they coincide, the solution is indeterminant. If they do not coincide and are parallel, we say the equations are inconsistent. A flowchart should help to sort out all of the above considerations. See Fig. 7-7 and program PØINT.

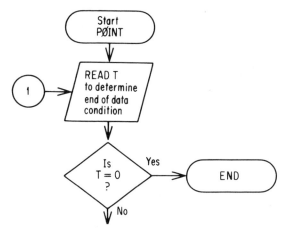

Figure 7-7 Flowchart for program POINT (cont'd on next page)

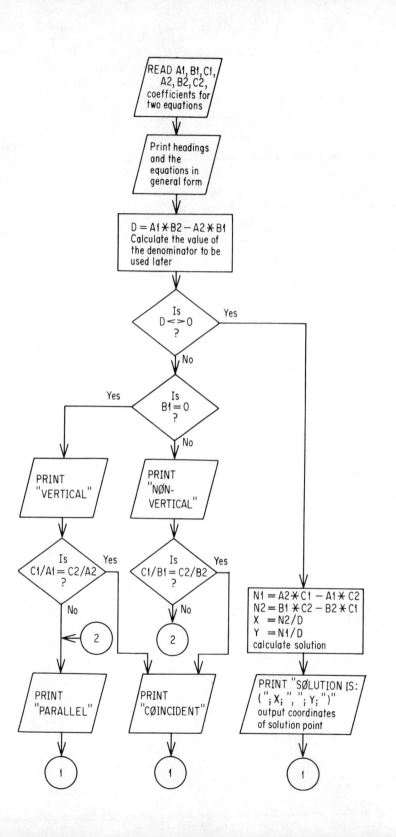

POINT

```
94    REM * THIS PROGRAM FINDS THE POINT OF INTERSECTION
95    REM   FOR TWO LINES GIVEN IN AX+BY+C=0 FORM. HANDLES
96    REM   INDETERMINANT AND INCONSISTENT CASES.
100   READ T
110      IF T = 0 THEN 500
112
114   REM * READ COEFFICIENTS FOR BOTH LINES
120   READ A1,B1,C1,  A2,B2,C2
130   PRINT
132
134   REM * PRINT THE EQUATIONS
140   PRINT  TAB(10); "LINES"
150   PRINT  A1; "*X+("; B1; ")*Y+("; C1; ") = 0"
160   PRINT  TAB(10); "AND"
170   PRINT  A2; "*X+("; B2; ")*Y+("; C2; ") = 0"
172
174   REM * IF A1*B2-A2*B1 <> 0 THEN THERE IS
175   REM   A UNIQUE SOLUTION
180   LET D = A1*B2 - A2*B1
190      IF D <> 0 THEN 300
192
194   REM * WE COULD TEST FOR B2 = 0 WITH THE SAME RESULT
200      IF B1 = 0 THEN 240
210   PRINT  "NON-VERTICAL ";
220      IF C1/B1 = C2/B2 THEN 280
230   GOTO 260
240   PRINT  "VERTICAL ";
250      IF C1/A1 = C2/A2 THEN 280
260   PRINT  "PARALLEL"
270   GOTO 100
280   PRINT  "COINCIDENT"
290   GOTO 100
292
294   REM * SOLUTION EXISTS - CALCULATE AND PRINT IT
300   LET N1 = A2*C1 - A1*C2
310   LET N2 = B1*C2 - B2*C1
320   LET X = N2/D
330   LET Y = N1/D
340   PRINT  "SOLUTION IS: ("; X; ","; Y; ")"
350   GOTO 100
352
394   REM
400   DATA  1,   1,1,1,   2,2,2
410   DATA  1,   1,2,3,   4,5,6
420   DATA  1,   3,0,4,   7,0,-8
430   DATA  1,   5,3,10,  10,6,-3
440   DATA  0
500   END
```

```
RUN
POINT


          LINES
  1     *X+( 1      )*Y+( 1      ) = 0
          AND
  2     *X+( 2      )*Y+( 2      ) = 0
NON-VERTICAL COINCIDENT

          LINES
  1     *X+( 2      )*Y+( 3      ) = 0
          AND
  4     *X+( 5      )*Y+( 6      ) = 0
SOLUTION IS: ( 1     ,-2     )
```

```
           LINES
  3     *X+( 0     )*Y+( 4    ) = 0
           AND
  7     *X+( 0     )*Y+(-8    ) = 0
VERTICAL PARALLEL

           LINES
  5     *X+( 3     )*Y+( 10   ) = 0
           AND
 10     *X+( 6     )*Y+(-3    ) = 0
NØN-VERTICAL PARALLEL
```

## Summary of Sec. 7-4

We have found the intersection of two lines for which the equations are given in standard form. Consideration has been given to the special cases of parallel and coincident lines.

## Problems for Sec. 7-4

1) Write a program to find the intersection of two lines with equations given in slope-intercept form.

2) Write a program to find the intersection of two lines given two points on each line.

3) Write a program to find the distance from a point to a line, given the equation of the line in $ax + by + c = 0$ form. You may use

$$d = \frac{|ax + by + c|}{\sqrt{a^2 + b^2}}$$

4) Write a program to find the distance from a point to a line, given two points on the line.

## 7-5 Three Points in a Plane

If we are given two points, we know that they lie on a straight line, but if we are given three points, they may or may not lie on a straight line, that is, they may or may not be collinear. If they are not collinear, there are many questions we may ask.

Let us look at three points, $A(x_1, y_1)$, $B(x_2, y_2)$ and $C(x_3, y_3)$, to determine if they are collinear. Suppose for the moment that if they are, the line containing them is not vertical. One way to see if they are collinear is to look at the slope of AB and the slope of BC. If the two slopes are equal, then the points are on a single line.

Now suppose that we select points (1, 2), (1, 4) and (2, 3) as DATA. Clearly the slope calculation will produce an undefined condition due to an attempt to divide by zero. We need to check for equal $x$-coordinates. We need only check $x_1 = x_2$ and $x_2 = x_3$. If $x_1 = x_2$, what about $x_1 - x_2$? Notice that $x_1 - x_2$ would be zero. Now we see that if $(x_1 - x_2)(x_2 - x_3) = 0$, then either AB or BC, or both, are vertical segments. Or, to put it another way, if $(x_1 - x_2)(x_2 - x_3)$ is not zero, then neither AB nor BC is vertical, and it is safe to instruct the computer to calculate the slopes of both segments. See especially line 190 in program CØLIN.

```
CØLIN

94   REM * THIS PRØGRAM DETERMINES WHEIHER ØR NØT
95   REM   THREE PØINTS IN A PLANE ARE CØLLINEAR.
96   REM   IT ALLØWS FØR PØINTS IN A VERTICAL LINE.
100  READ T
110     IF T = 0 THEN 900
120  PRINT
130  READ X1,Y1,  X2,Y2,  X3,Y3
140  PRINT   "(";  X1;  ",";  Y1;  "),";
150  PRINT   "(";  X2;  ",";  Y2;  ") AND ";
160  PRINT   "(";  X3;  ",";  Y3;  ")"
170  LET D1 = X1-X2
180  LET D2 = X2-X3
182
184  REM * IF D1*D2 NØN-ZERØ THEN NEITHER
185  REM   SEGMENT IS VERTICAL
190     IF D1*D2 <> 0 THEN 300
200     IF D1 <> 0 THEN 400
210     IF D2 <> 0 THEN 400
212
214  REM * AT THIS PØINT BØTH SEGMENTS ARE VERTICAL
220  PRINT   "VERTICALLY CØLLINEAR"
230  GØTØ 100
292
294  REM * CALCULATE BØTH SLØPES
300  LET M1 = (Y1-Y2)/D1
310  LET M2 = (Y2-Y3)/D2
312
314  REM * IF SLØPES NØT EQUAL THEN PØINTS NØN-CØLLINEAR
320     IF M1 <> M2 THEN 400
330  PRINT   "CØLLINEAR"
340  GØTØ 100
400  PRINT   "NØN-CØLLINEAR"
410  GØTØ 100
492
494  REM
500  DATA  1,   6,5,   0,7,  -9,10
510  DATA  1,   1,2,   3,4,   5,7
520  DATA  1,   1,2,   1,4,   2,3
530  DATA  1,   5,2,   5,-3,  5,50
540  DATA  0
900  END
RUN
CØLIN


( 6    , 5    ),( 0    , 7    ) AND (-9    , 10   )
CØLLINEAR

( 1    , 2    ),( 3    , 4    ) AND ( 5    , 7    )
NØN-CØLLINEAR

( 1    , 2    ),( 1    , 4    ) AND ( 2    , 3    )
NØN-CØLLINEAR

( 5    , 2    ),( 5    ,-3    ) AND ( 5    , 50   )
VERTICALLY CØLLINEAR
```

## Triangles *(The Noncollinear Case)*

It should be clear that if three points in a plane are noncollinear, they are vertices of a triangle. That being the case, we have a whole new collection of properties to consider. To name only a few possibilities, we can calculate the area using Hero's formula; we can test to see if the triangle is acute, right, or obtuse; we can find the centroid where the medians intersect; we can find the orthocenter where the altitudes intersect; and we can find the lengths of the altitudes.

Suppose we first look for a right triangle. There are at least two procedures we might use. One is to test the lengths of the three sides using the Pythagorean Theorem, $c^2 = a^2 + b^2$. Another is to test the slope of each pair of sides to see if their product is $-1$ or if one side is vertical and another is horizontal. Either procedure will be instructive. Let's first investigate Pythagoras with the aid of Fig. 7-8.

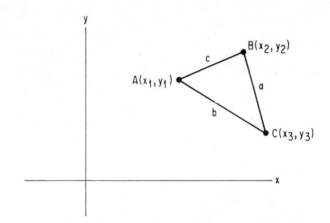

**Figure 7-8**

When we consider $c^2 = a^2 + b^2$ we assume that the hypotenuse has length $c$. Suppose we find that $a$ is the length of the hypotenuse or that $b$ is. The only safe bet is to test them all. This could be done by putting the following in an IF-THEN statement to test if AB is the hypotenuse for points $A(x_1, y_1)$, $B(x_2, y_2)$ and $C(x_3, y_3)$:

$$(X1 - X2)\uparrow2 + (Y1 - Y2)\uparrow2 = ((X2 - X3)\uparrow2 + (Y2 - Y3)\uparrow2)$$
$$+ ((X3 - X1)\uparrow2 + (Y3 - Y1)\uparrow2)$$

and by then putting in two similar statements to see if BC or CA might be the hypotenuse. Such a procedure ought to work, but this statement is excessively long and cumbersome and we aren't really using the power of the computer to do repeated operations. It seems worthwhile to devise a way of storing the coordinates so that we can use computer loops to move around the triangle instead of writing new statements for each side being considered. That seems to suggest subscripts and lists. So instead of X1, X2, and X3 we are going to use X(1), X(2), and X(3). And for Y1, Y2, and Y3 we use Y(1), Y(2), and Y(3), as shown in Fig. 7-9.

Often when trying a new procedure on a new program, it is a good idea to do the work piecemeal. If we put a lot of new things into a program simultaneously, errors are harder to find than if we go in steps. Consider program PYTH1 for simply reading coordinates in and printing them out.

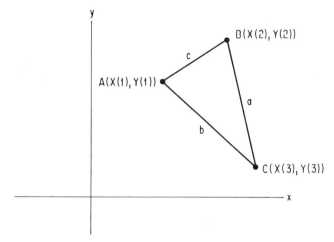

**Figure 7-9**

PYTH1

```
94      REM * THIS IS A TRIAL PRØGRAM TØ SIMPLY READ
95      REM   CØØRDINATES FØR THE VERTICES ØF A TRIANGLE
96      REM   AND PRINT THEM ØUT AGAIN USING AN X LIST
97      REM   FØR X CØØRDINATES AND A Y LIST FØR Y
98      REM   CØØRDINATES
100     DIM X(3), Y(3)
110     READ T
120        IF T = 0 THEN 900
130     PRINT
132
134     REM * READ CØØRDINATES IN LINES 140 TØ 160
140     FØR P = 1 TØ 3
150        READ X(P), Y(P)
160     NEXT P
162
164     REM * PRINT CØØRDINATES IN LINES 170 TØ 190
170     PRINT   "("; X(1); ","; Y(1); ")","";
180     PRINT   "("; X(2); ","; Y(2); ") AND ";
190     PRINT   "("; X(3); ","; Y(3); ")"
200     GØTØ 110
792
794     REM
800     DATA 1,    1,2,    5,-1,    6,15
810     DATA 1,    0,0,    0,3,     4,0
820     DATA 0
900     END
RUN
PYTH1
```

```
( 1    , 2    ),( 5    ,-1    ) AND ( 6    , 15    )
( 0    , 0    ),( 0    , 3    ) AND ( 4    , 0    )
```

To consider each side in turn as a possible hypotenuse, we want to work our way around the triangle. First we will use the distance from point 1 to point 2, then the distance from point 2 to point 3, and finally the distance from point 3 to point 1. See the columns labeled "Hypotenuse" in Table 7-1.

**TABLE 7-1**

| Hypotenuse | | 1st Leg | | 2nd Leg | |
|---|---|---|---|---|---|
| Segment | Points | Segment | Points | Segment | Points |
| AB | 1,2 | BC | 2,3 | CA | 3,1 |
| BC | 2,3 | CA | 3,1 | AB | 1,2 |
| CA | 3,1 | AB | 1,2 | BC | 2,3 |

Looking at Table 7-1, we see a progression across, from points 1 and 2 to points 2 and 3 and then to points 3 and 1 for hypotenuse AB. For hypotenuse BC, we go from points 2 and 3 to points 3 and 1 and then to points 1 and 2. This pattern is completed by considering CA as the hypotenuse. If we can simply go 1-2-3-1-2-3, we can get all of the pairs we need using loops and subscripts. Consider the following four lines of BASIC code:

```
200   FØR P = 1 TØ 3
210       LET X(P+3) = X(P)
220       LET Y(P+3) = Y(P)
230   NEXT P
```

These four lines have the effect of copying the three points 1, 2, and 3 into locations 4, 5, and 6, respectively, of the X and Y lists. This will enable us to organize the testing of each side in turn for being the hypotenuse of triangle ABC, as shown in TABLE 7-1. See lines 200 to 230 in PYTH2.

```
PYTH2
94    REM * THIS PRØGRAM STØRES THE CØRDINATES ØF THE
95    REM   VERTICES ØF A TRIANGLE IN THE FIRST THREE
96    REM   ELEMENTS ØF X AND Y LISTS AND DUPLICATED
97    REM   IN THE NEXT THREE ELEMENTS ØF THØSE LISTS
98    REM   TØ FACILITATE USE ØF SUBSCRIPTS AND LØØPS
99    REM   TØ TEST PRØPERTIES ØF THE TRIANGLES.
100   DIM X(6), Y(6)
110   READ T
120       IF T = 0 THEN 900
130   PRINT
132
134   REM * READ CØØRDINATES IN LINES 140 TØ 160
140   FØR P = 1 TØ 3
150       READ X(P), Y(P)
160   NEXT P
162
164   REM * PRINT CØØRDINATES IN LINES 170 TØ 190
170   PRINT   "("; X(1); ","; Y(1); "),";
180   PRINT   "("; X(2); ","; Y(2); ") AND ";
190   PRINT   "("; X(3); ","; Y(3); ")"
192
194   REM * DUPLICATIØN TAKES PLACE IN LINES 200 TØ 230
200   FØR P = 1 TØ 3
210       LET X(P+3) = X(P)
220       LET Y(P+3) = Y(P)
230   NEXT P
232
234   REM * WE PRINT THE CØNTENTS ØF THE X AND Y LISTS
235   REM   FØR DEMØNSTRATIØN PURPØSES ØNLY
```

```
240   PRINT  "VALUES ØF X LØØK LIKE THIS IN THE X LIST"
250   FØR P = 1 TØ 6
260       PRINT X(P);
270   NEXT P
280   PRINT
282
290   PRINT  "VALUES ØF Y LØØK LIKE THIS IN THE Y LIST"
300   FØR P = 1 TØ 6
310       PRINT Y(P);
320   NEXT P
330   PRINT
332
340   GØTØ 110
792
794   REM
800   DATA  1,    1,2,    5,-1,    6,15
810   DATA  1,    0,0,    0,3,    4,0
820   DATA  0
900   END
RUN
PYTH2


( 1    , 2    ),( 5    ,-1    ) AND ( 6    , 15   )
VALUES ØF X LØØK LIKE THIS IN THE X LIST
  1    5    6    1    5    6
VALUES ØF Y LØØK LIKE THIS IN THE Y LIST
  2    -1    15    2    -1    15

( 0    , 0    ),( 0    , 3    ) AND ( 4    , 0    )
VALUES ØF X LØØK LIKE THIS IN THE X LIST
  0    0    4    0    0    4
VALUES ØF Y LØØK LIKE THIS IN THE Y LIST
  0    3    0    0    3    0
```

Now all that remains is to calculate the lengths of the sides of the triangle and to store them in such a way that we may test in sequence around the triangle, trying each side as possible hypotenuse. This is accomplished by lines 300 to 350 in PYTH3. Note that line 340 does for the lengths of sides what 210 and 220 do for the coordinates of the vertices.

```
PYTH3

94    REM * THIS PRØGRAM DETERMINES FRØM THE CØØRDINATES
95    REM   ØF THE VERTICES ØF A TRIANGLE WHETHER ØR
96    REM   NØT IT IS A RIGHT TRIANGLE
100   DIM X(6), Y(6), D(6)
110   READ T
120     IF T = 0 THEN 900
130   PRINT
132
134   REM * READ CØØRDINATES IN LINES 140 TØ 160
140   FØR P = 1 TØ 3
150       READ X(P), Y(P)
160   NEXT P
162
164   REM * PRINT CØØRDINATES IN LINES 170 TØ 190
170   PRINT  "(";  X(1);  ",";  Y(1);  "),";
180   PRINT  "(";  X(2);  ",";  Y(2);  ") AND ";
190   PRINT  "(";  X(3);  ",";  Y(3);  ")"
192
194   REM * DUPLICATIØN TAKES PLACE IN LINES 200 TØ 230
200   FØR P = 1 TØ 3
210       LET X(P+3) = X(P)
220       LET Y(P+3) = Y(P)
230   NEXT P
232
```

```
294   REM * ENTER LENGTHS IN THE D LIST IN THE
295   REM   SAME FØRMAT AS USED FØR CØØRDINATES IN
296   REM   THE X AND Y LISTS; THAT IS - DUPLICATED
300   FØR J = 1 TØ 3
310      LET A = X(J)-X(J+1)
320      LET B = Y(J)-Y(J+1)
330      LET D(J) = SQR( A↑2+B↑2 )
340      LET D(J+3) = D(J)
350   NEXT J
352
394   REM * NØW TEST EACH SIDE FØR BEING A HYPØTENUSE
400   FØR P = 1 TØ 3
410      IF D(P)↑2 = D(P+1)↑2 + D(P+2)↑2 THEN 500
420   NEXT P
422
424   REM * IF THE TEST FAILS FØR ALL THREE SIDES THEN
425   REM   WE HAVE A NØN-RIGHT TRIANGLE
430   PRINT   "NØT A RIGHT TRIANGLE"
440   GØTØ 110
492
500   PRINT   "RIGHT TRIANGLE WITH HYPØTENUSE DETERMINED BY"
510   PRINT   "PØINTS: ("; X(P); ","; Y(P); ") AND ";
520   PRINT   "("; X(P+1); ","; Y(P+1); ")"
530   GØTØ 110
792
794   REM
800   DATA  1,    1,2,    5,-1,   6,15
810   DATA  1,    0,0,    0,3,    4,0
820   DATA  0
900   END
RUN
PYTH3


( 1    , 2    ),( 5    ,-1    ) AND ( 6    , 15   )
NØT A RIGHT TRIANGLE

( 0    , 0    ),( 0    , 3    ) AND ( 4    , 0    )
RIGHT TRIANGLE WITH HYPØTENUSE DETERMINED BY
PØINTS: ( 0    , 3    ) AND ( 4    , 0    )
```

## Summary of Sec. 7-5

We have examined sets of three points for collinearity. We have looked at the triangle formed by noncollinear points to determine whether or not it is a right triangle. In order to do this, we have devised a technique of storing coordinates in lists to take advantage of repeatable program statements using loops.

## Problems for Sec. 7-5

1) In program CØLIN, provide for treating points on a horizontal line as a special case.
2) Write a program to find the intersection of two altitudes of a triangle.
3) Write a program to find the intersection of two medians of a triangle.
4) Modify program PYTH3 to classify triangles as acute, equiangular, right, or obtuse.
5) Have the computer print all Pythagorean Triples for a hypotenuse less than 101. Pay particular attention to efficiency here.
6) Write a program to determine if four points are collinear.
7) Write a program to determine if $n$ points are collinear.

8) Write a program to compute the area of a triangle given the co-ordinates of the three vertices and using Hero's formula:

$$A = \sqrt{s(s - a)(s - b)(s - c)} \qquad \text{where} \qquad s = (a + b + c)/2$$

9) Write a program to calculate the area of a triangle by finding the length of an altitude using the methods of Sec. 7-4.

10) Write a program to test triangles for right triangles by determining the slope of all three sides to see if the product is $-1$ for any pair. You will have to treat vertical lines as a special case.

11) Given three noncollinear points, find the center and radius of the circle they determine.

# 8
# POLYNOMIALS

## 8-1 Introduction

A real polynomial in $x$ can be defined as any expression that can be written in the following form:

$$a_n x^n + a_{n-1} x^{n-1} + \cdots + a_2 x^2 + a_1 x + a_0$$

For a given value of $x$, $n$ is a non-negative integer and the $a$'s are constant values. Examples of polynomials are

$$2x; \quad 3x^2 + 2; \quad 4; \quad 5x^{11} + 3x^3 - 2$$

The highest exponent of $x$, called $n$, is the degree of the polynomial.

Polynomials are of interest to the mathematician and scientist alike. The distance an object travels in a gravitational field is described by a second degree polynomial, for example. We will now explore some ways in which the computer may be programmed to evaluate polynomials and make some comparisons.

Regardless of the final procedure to be used to evaluate a polynomial, we will probably want to store the coefficients in a list. If you have zero subscripts available, this is a perfect fit because the subscript of the coefficient is equal to the exponent on $x$ in each term. If you don't use zero subscripts, simply adjust the variable used for exponents. We arbitrarily select $3x^4 + 2x^3 - x^2 + 5x + 3$ for our first example. The degree of the example is four, and hence there are five coefficients. The coefficients and the degree of the polynomial may be entered as data.

One procedure for evaluating a polynomial is to use a BASIC language function such as

```
100   DEF FNP(X) = P(5)*X↑4+P(4)*X↑3+P(3)*X↑2+P(2)*X+P(1)
```

This defined function will work fine for any fourth degree polynomial. For a degree less than four we could fill in with zeros, but for degrees more than four, we would have to retype the line. We are also limited by line length when DEFining a function on some computer systems. Others allow multiple line DEFinitions. So while the DEF capability is very useful in some situations, we might give some thought to developing another procedure for evaluating a polynomial.

Note that the exponent of $x$ is one less than the subscript of the list coefficient in each term of the DEF statement. (They are the same if you use zero subscripts.) Even $p(2)*x$ can be written $p(2)*x\uparrow 1$ and $p(1)$ can be written $p(1)*x\uparrow 0$ (unless $x = 0$). This suggests the following loop:

```
300     LET P2 = P(1)
310     FØR I = N+1 TØ 2 STEP -1
320         LET P2 = P2 + P(I)*X↑(I-1)
330     NEXT I
```

This four line routine has the desirable feature that it requires no change for handling polynomials of differing degree.

Suppose we give some thought to the number of operations we are instructing the computer to perform. Look at line 320. There we can see an addition and a multiplication and an exponentiation. For positive integers as exponents, exponentiation amounts to successive multiplication. That means for an exponent of $I - 1$ there will be $I - 2$ multiplications plus the multiplication of the coefficient. That makes $I - 1$ multiplications for that line. If we take another look at $3x^4 + 2x^3 - x^2 + 4x + 3$ and count the number of operations, we get four additions and 10 multiplications for our fourth degree polynomial (not accounting for how the computer might handle the exponent one as a special case). For a $10^{th}$ degree polynomial there would be 10 additions and 55 multiplications.

Programmers often try to improve the efficiency of their programs because of the limitations of the computer and the size of the job to be done or purely for the challenge involved. Notice that in any polynomial, beginning with the second term, each term has $x$ as a factor one less time than the previous term. This suggests some sort of successive factoring, as shown by the following:

$$3x^4 + 2x^3 = (3x + 2)x^3$$

$$(3x + 2)x^3 - x^2 = ((3x + 2)x - 1)x^2$$

$$((3x + 2)x - 1)x^2 + 4x = (((3x + 2)x - 1)x + 4)x$$

$$(((3x + 2)x - 1)x + 4)x + 3 = (((3x + 2)x - 1)x + 4)x + 3$$

Thus our original polynomial $3x^4 + 2x^3 - x^2 + 4x + 3$ can be written in the following form:

$$(((3x + 2)x - 1)x + 4)x + 3$$

This is called nested form.

Now there are only four multiplications and four additions called for in a fourth degree polynomial. Of course, a saving of six multiplications is not much to a computer, but the saving accumulates as the degree of the polynomial in-

Polynomials 103

creases and as the number of times we evaluate the polynomial increases. Consider the following routine:

```
400    LET P3 = P(N+1)
410    FØR I = N TØ 1 STEP -1
420      LET P3 = P3*X + P(I)
430    NEXT I
```

We have another four-line routine that is more efficient than the first one.

We now have three procedures for evaluating polynomials. The first is a defined function, the second is a loop which evaluates the polynomial using exponents term by term, and the third is a loop which uses nested form. Let's assemble these three procedures into a program so that we can compare some values. As we expected, we see that all values do check out by looking at the output of program PØLY01.

```
PØLY01

94    REM * THIS PRØGRAM EVALUATES PØLYNØMIALS BY THREE
95    REM   METHØDS; DEF, TERM BY TERM AND NESTING
96
97    REM * SET UP DEFINED FUNCTION
100   DEF FNP(X) = P(5)*X↑4+P(4)*X↑3+P(3)*X↑2+P(2)*X+P(1)
102
104   REM * READ DATA
110   READ N
120   FØR I = N+1 TØ 1 STEP -1
130     READ P(I)
140   NEXT I
142
144   REM * PRINT HEADINGS
150   PRINT  "X", "FNP(X)", "EXP LØØP", "NESTING"
160   FØR X = 1 TØ 10
192
194   REM * CALCULATE BY DEF
200     LET P1 = FNP(X)
292
294     REM * CALCULATE USING EXPØNENTS IN A LØØP
295     REM   TERM BY TERM
300     LET P2 = P(1)
310     FØR I = N+1 TØ 2 STEP -1
320       LET P2 = P2 + P(I)*X↑(I-1)
330     NEXT I
392
394     REM * CALCULATE USING NESTING
400     LET P3 = P(N+1)
410     FØR I = N TØ 1 STEP -1
420       LET P3 = P3*X + P(I)
430     NEXT I
492
494     REM * PRINT RESULTS
500       PRINT X, P1, P2, P3
510   NEXT X
512
514   REM
520   DATA  4, 3, 2, -1, 5, 3
530   END
RUN
PØLY01
```

| X | FNP(X) | EXP LØØP | NESTING |
|---|--------|----------|---------|
| 1 | 12 | 12 | 12 |
| 2 | 73 | 73 | 73 |
| 3 | 306 | 306 | 306 |
| 4 | 903 | 903 | 903 |

| 5  | 2128  | 2128  | 2128  |
|----|-------|-------|-------|
| 6  | 4317  | 4317  | 4317  |
| 7  | 7878  | 7878  | 7878  |
| 8  | 13291 | 13291 | 13291 |
| 9  | 21108 | 21108 | 21108 |
| 10 | 31953 | 31953 | 31953 |

## Problems for Sec. 8-1

1) Write a program to tabulate the number of additions and multiplications for varying degrees of polynomial in order to compare nesting with a one line DEF or with a loop which uses exponents.
2) Write a program to multiply two polynomials.
3) Write a program to add polynomials. Be sure to avoid leading zero coefficients.
4) Do problem 3 for subtraction.
5) Write a program to give ordered pairs $(x, p(x))$ suitable for graphing the polynomial $p(x)$.
6) Write a program to find zeros of a second-degree polynomial using the quadratic formula.

## 8-2   Finding a Real Zero of a Polynomial

Now that we are set up to evaluate a polynomial, we can explore some applications. One important consideration where polynomials are concerned is to find values of $x$ for which the value of the polynomial is equal to zero. If we designate a polynomial as $p(x)$ (read $p$ of $x$) and set $y$ equal to $p(x)$, then we may think in terms of polynomial equations and their graphs. The zeros of a polynomial are the values of $x$ where $p(x) = 0$. For real zeros they are the values of $x$ where the graph of the polynomial equation crosses the $x$-axis. However, in the case of nonreal zeros, while the value of $p(x)$ will be zero, the graph of the polynomial equation in the $x$-$y$ plane will not cross the $x$-axis. Of course, we are familiar with special mathematical procedures for solving certain polynomials. For instance, all second-degree polynomials may be solved by the quadratic formula. We will look here at more general solutions.

It can be shown that every $n$th degree polynomial has exactly $n$ complex zeros. So one approach to finding zeros is to simply try values of $x$ until $n$ are found which give $p(x) = 0$. Such a procedure is feasible only with the aid of a computer because of the tedious calculations required. Even so, the approach can be very complicated indeed. We will simplify our job for now if we begin by looking only for real zeros. A most valuable aid to finding zeros of any continuous function $y = f(x)$ is the principle that if $f(x_1)$ and $f(x_2)$ are of different sign, then there are an odd number of zeros in the interval from $x_1$ to $x_2$. For real values of $x$ it should be clear that if $f(x_1) > 0$, the point $(x_1, f(x_1))$ on the graph is above the $x$-axis, whereas $f(x_1) < 0$ makes $(x_2, f(x_2))$ below the $x$-axis, and the graph of a continuous function must cross the $x$-axis somewhere in between.

There is a variety of ways to isolate increments in which real zeros may be found. Let us set up a procedure whereby we have control over where the computer searches for intervals within which zeros may be found. We can store coefficients in a list, select limits within which to search, and have the computer step through the specified region, trying pairs of values for $x$ to see if $f(x_1)*f(x_2)$ is positive. If it is not, then we have a zero between $x_1$ and $x_2$ or either $x_1$ or $x_2$ is a zero. If we always find $f(x_1)*f(x_2)$ positive, there are numerous possible reasons. We may not have included the zeros in our limits, or we may have had the computer search such large increments that the graph crosses the $x$-axis an even number of times, or the graph may just touch the $x$-axis at a minimum or maximum point and never cross the $x$-axis (the point at which it touches, however, is still a zero of the polynomial), or there are no real zeros. We must bear all of these problems in mind as we construct and operate a program.

In program ZERØ01, line 120 reads the degree of the polynomial and line 140 reads the coefficients. Line 280 tests for sign change. The subroutine which starts at line 800 evaluates the polynomial by nesting. Line 840 checks for exact zeros. The general procedure here is just as valid for any continuous function as it is for polynomial functions. Note that we could use the graphing of Chapter 5 to assist us in finding regions where we might expect to find zeros.

ZERØ01

```
      94    REM * THIS PRØGRAM SEARCHES FØR A SIGN CHANGE
      95    REM   IN THE VALUE ØF A PØLYNØMIAL FUNCTIØN
     100    DIM   P(15)
     110    PRINT  "PØLYNØMIAL IS";
 ──► 120    READ N
     130    FØR I = N+1 TØ 1 STEP -1
 ──► 140        READ P(I)
     150        PRINT  P(I);
     160    NEXT I
     162
     170    PRINT
     180    PRINT
     190    PRINT  "FIRST, LAST, STEP";
     200    INPUT F, L, S
     210    PRINT
     220    LET X0 = F
     230    GØSUB 800
     240    FØR X = F+S TØ L STEP S
     242
     244    REM * SAVE THE VALUE ØF THE FUNCTIØN AT THE
     245    REM   BEGINNING ØF THE INTERVAL
     250        LET Y1 = P3
     260        LET X0 = X
     270        GØSUB 800
 ──► 280        IF Y1*P3 > 0 THEN 320
     290    PRINT  "SIGN CHANGE:"
     300    PRINT  "P("; X-S; ")="; Y1; "AND P("; X; ")="; P3
     310    STØP
     320    NEXT X
     322
     330    PRINT  "NØ SIGN CHANGE FØUND"
     340    STØP
     792
     794    REM * LINES 800 TØ 830 EVALUATE BY NESTING
 ──► 800    LET P3 = P(N+1)
     810    FØR I = N TØ 1 STEP -1
     820        LET P3 = P3*X0 + P(I)
     830    NEXT I
     832
     834    REM * CHECK FØR EXACT ZERO
 ──► 840        IF P3 <> 0 THEN 880
     850    PRINT
     860    PRINT  X0; "IS A ZERO"
     870    STØP
     880    RETURN
     882
```

```
884   REM
890   DATA   3,   1,2,3,4
900   END
RUN
ZER001

POLYNOMIAL IS 1   2   3   4

FIRST, LAST, STEP?  -10,10,1

SIGN CHANGE:
P(-2 )=-2 AND P(-1 )= 2
```

## Interval Halving

Now we have an interval in which we expect to find a zero. We would like to make that interval smaller and smaller to get successively better approximations of a zero. We can simply evaluate the polynomial at the midpoint of the interval found in program ZER∅01 and check for a change of sign against one endpoint. If a change in sign is found, we bisect and repeat. If a change in sign is not found, then the change must occur between the midpoint and the endpoint not tested above; therefore we bisect that interval and repeat. After each bisection the interval is smaller and the midpoint is a better approximation of the zero. This process is accomplished in lines 400 to 550 of program ZER∅02.

The process needs a stopping place. We need a test of the accuracy of the current approximation that works for roots very close to zero and far away from zero, a test, moreover, that is compatible with the precision of the computer. We would like to get six significant digits in our results. We label the endpoints of the interval $x_1$ and $x_2$. If we test $|x_1 - x_2|$ against $10^{-6}$, we will not get six significant digits for $x_1$ and $x_2$ when they are very close to zero. For $x_1$ and $x_2$ large in magnitude, say 100,000, we would require a machine with 12-digit precision. These problems are avoided by using relative error and testing $|x_1 - x_2|/(|x_1| + |x_2|)$ against $10^{-6}$. See line 450 in program ZER∅02.

```
ZER002

94    REM * THIS PROGRAM SEARCHES FOR APPROXIMATE ZEROS
95    REM   IN THE INTERVALS FOUND IN PROGRAM ZERO01
100   DIM   P(15)
110   PRINT   "POLYNOMIAL IS";
120   READ N
130   FOR I = N+1 TO 1 STEP -1
140       READ P(I)
150       PRINT  P(I);
160   NEXT I
162
170   PRINT
180   PRINT
190   PRINT   "FIRST, LAST, STEP";
200   INPUT F, L, S
210   PRINT
220   LET X0 = F
230   GOSUB 800
240   FOR X = F+S TO L STEP S
250       LET Y1 = P3
260       LET X0 = X
270       GOSUB 800
280           IF Y1*P3 > 0 THEN 320
```

```
290     PRINT  "SIGN CHANGE:"
300     PRINT  "P(";  X-S;  ")=";  Y1;  "AND P(";  X;  ")=";  P3
310     GOTO  400
320  NEXT X
322
330  PRINT  "NO SIGN CHANGE FOUND"
340  STOP
392
394  REM * LINES 400 THROUGH 550 CARRY OUT INTERVAL
395  REM   HALVING. INTERVAL BOUNDARIES ARE X1 AND X2
396  REM   EXACT ZEROS ARE FOUND IN LINE 840
400  LET X1 = X-S
410  LET X2 = X
420  LET Y2 = P3
422
424  REM * HALVING TAKES PLACE IN LINE 430
430  LET X0 = (X1+X2)/2
440  GOSUB 800
450     IF ABS(X1-X2)/(ABS(X1)+ABS(X2)) > 1E-6 THEN 500
460  PRINT
470  PRINT  "APPROXIMATE ZERO:"
480  PRINT  "P(";  X0;  ")=";  P3
490  STOP
500     IF Y1*P3 > 0 THEN 530
510  LET X2 = X0
520  GOTO 420
530  LET X1 = X0
540  LET Y1 = P3
550  GOTO 430
792
794  REM * EVALUATE BY NESTING
800  LET P3 = P(N+1)
810  FOR I = N TO 1 STEP -1
820     LET P3 = P3*X0 + P(I)
830  NEXT I
832
840     IF P3 <> 0 THEN 880
850  PRINT
860  PRINT  X0;  "IS A ZERO"
870  STOP
880  RETURN
882
884  REM
890  DATA  3,  1,2,3,4
900  END
RUN
ZERO 02

POLYNOMIAL IS 1  2  3  4

FIRST, LAST, STEP? -2,-1,.1

SIGN CHANGE:
P(-1.7 )=-0.233 AND P(-1.6 )= 0.224

APPROXIMATE ZERO:
P(-1.65063 )=-4.7632E-6
```

## Summary of Sec. 8-2

We have used the principle that if $f(x_1)$ and $f(x_2)$ are of opposite signs, there must be a value of $x$ between $x_1$ and $x_2$ such that $f(x) = 0$ if we are to find intervals within which zeros exist for polynomial functions. We have further reduced interval size by successive halving to obtain approximate zeros. All of the methods used here can easily be applied to other finite continuous functions as well.

## Problems for Sec. 8-2

1) Find a zero for any or all of the following:
   a) $x^3 + 6x^2 - 49x + 66$
   b) $x^4 + 2x^3 - 13x^2 - 14x + 24$
   c) $x^3 + 11x^2 - 68x - 672$
   d) $2x^3 + 3x^2 + 4x - 5$
   e) $x^5 + 13x^4 - 37x^3 - 457x^2 + 492x + 2340$
   f) $x^3 + 2x^2 - 11x - 12$
   g) $x^5 + 4.8x^4 - 4.2x^3 - 29.6x^2 + 7.2x + 28.8$

2) Modify ZER∅02 to search for all real zeros automatically after the values of $F$, $L$, and $S$ have been specified. Be sure to stop if all zeros have been found without further testing values of $x$.

3) Modify ZER∅02 to use linear interpolation instead of interval halving to obtain approximate zeros.

4) Modify ZER∅02 to find zeros for any continuous function rather than just a polynomial function.

## 8-3  Synthetic Division to Get Further Zeros

We present the Remainder Theorem, Factor Theorem, and synthetic division as aids to finding zeros after a first zero is known.

### The Remainder Theorem

If $p(x)$ is divided by $(x - z)$, the remainder is the value of the polynomial when $z$ is substituted for $x$.

$$\frac{p(x)}{(x - z)} = q(x) + \frac{r}{(x - z)}$$

That is, $p(x)$ divided by $(x - z)$ yields a quotient polynomial plus a remainder. Multiplying through by $(x - z)$ we get:

$$p(x) = (x - z)q(x) + r$$

and when $z$ is substituted for $x$ that produces:

$$p(z) = (z - z)q(z) + r$$

or simply

$$p(z) = r$$

### Factor Theorem

We note that when the value of $r$ is zero, we have $p(z) = 0$, and that makes $z$ a solution of the equation $p(x) = 0$ or a zero of the polynomial. Since the remainder is zero after dividing by $(x - z)$, it follows that $(x - z)$ must be a factor of $p(x)$, or

$$p(x) = (x - z)q(x)$$

Having found the first zero using the procedure of Sec. 8-2, we need only find

$q(x)$ and then use the procedure of 8-2 on it, repeating until all real zeros are found.

## Synthetic Division

We now develop the synthetic division algorithm using $x^4 + 5x^3 + 9x^2 + 8x + 4$ divided by $x + 2$ as an example. It is this division that will enable us to find $q(x)$ above. We begin by performing the division "long hand":

$$
\begin{array}{r}
x^3 + 3x^2 + 3x + 2 \\
x + 2 \overline{)\ x^4 + 5x^3 + 9x^2 + 8x + 4} \\
\underline{x^4 + 2x^3} \\
3x^3 + 9x^2 \\
\underline{3x^3 + 6x^2} \\
3x^2 + 8x \\
\underline{3x^2 + 6x} \\
2x + 4 \\
\underline{2x + 4}
\end{array}
$$

Notice that a great many things will always be written twice. We will always "bring down" $9x^2$ and $8x$ and 4. For division by $x + 2$, we will always get $x^4$ and $3x^3$ and $3x^2$ and $2x$ repeated. So let us eliminate these repetitions and compress the problem vertically:

$$
\begin{array}{r}
x^3 + 3x^2 + 3x + 2 \\
x + 2 \overline{)\ x^4 + 5x^3 + 9x^2 + 8x + 4} \\
2x^3 + 6x^2 + 6x + 4 \\
\hline
3x^3 + 3x^2 + 2x
\end{array}
$$

Now if we line things up properly, there is no need to write the $x$'s and their exponents. And there will always be an $x$ in the divisor, so we don't need that. Let's condense again:

$$
\begin{array}{r}
1 + 3 + 3 + 2 \\
+ 2 \overline{)\ 1 + 5 + 9 + 8 + 4} \\
2 + 6 + 6 + 4 \\
\hline
3 + 3 + 2
\end{array}
$$

Since the coefficient of the first term of the quotient is always the same as the coefficient of the first term of the original polynomial, we can make the bottom line of figures exactly agree with the top line by simply bringing down the first figure. Now we eliminate the top line to get:

$$
\begin{array}{r}
+ 2 \overline{)\ 1 + 5 + 9 + 8 + 4} \\
2 + 6 + 6 + 4 \\
\hline
1 + 3 + 3 + 2
\end{array}
$$

Recognizing that subtraction is the same as "changing the sign and adding," we can change the 2 to a $-2$ and add instead of subtracting. That leaves us with:

$$
\begin{array}{r}
- \, 2\overline{)1 + 5 + 9 + 8 + 4} \\
- \, 2 - 6 - 6 - 4 \\
\hline
1 + 3 + 3 + 2
\end{array}
$$

The sequence of operations is as follows: Bring down the 1, multiply the 1 by $-2$, and write it under the 5. Add 5 and $-2$ to get 3. Multiply the 3 by $-2$ and write it down under the 9. Add 9 and $-6$ to get 3. Multiply 3 by $-2$ and write it down under the 8. Add 8 and $-6$ to get 2. Multiply 2 by $-2$ and write it down under the 4. Add 4 and $-4$ to get a remainder of 0. Division done by this algorithm is called "synthetic division."

Since synthetic division is an iterative process, it is especially suited to the computer. Notice that most of the process consists of multiplying and adding. Not only is that an iterative process, but it is the same iterative process used for evaluating polynomials by the nesting method. All that is required to adapt the subroutine 800 in program ZERØ02 to synthetic division is to store the subtotals along the way in an appropriate list element. This is done in line 820 of program DIVIDE. Look at program DIVIDE and compare subroutine 800 in it with the subroutine 800 in ZERØ02.

```
DIVIDE

94    REM * THIS PROGRAM USES SYNTHETIC DIVISION
100   DIM P(15), Q(15)
110   READ N
120   PRINT   "P(X)=";
130   FØR I = N+1 TO 1 STEP -1
140      READ P(I)
150      PRINT  P(I);
160   NEXT I
162
170   PRINT
180   PRINT  "DIVIDE BY X-";
190   INPUT  X0
200   PRINT  "QUØTIENT ";
210   GØSUB 800
220   STØP
792
794   REM * THE DIVISIØN TAKES PLACE IN LINES 800 TO 830
795   REM * NOTE THE SIMILARITY TO NESTING
800   LET P3 = Q(N+1) = P(N+1)
810   FØR I = N TO 1 STEP -1
→ 820      LET Q(I) = P3 = P3*X0 + P(I)
830   NEXT I
832
834   REM * PRINT RESULTS
840   FØR I = N+1 TO 2 STEP -1
850      PRINT Q(I);
860   NEXT I
862
870   PRINT  "REMAINDER =";  Q(1)
880   RETURN
882
884   REM
890   DATA  4,  1,5,9,8,4
900   END
```

```
RUN
DIVIDE

P(X)= 1   5   9   8   4
DIVIDE BY X-?  -2
QUOTIENT  1   3   3   2 REMAINDER = 0
```

Program DIVIDE works well, but why use a program to perform division in the first place? Why not simply use program ZER∅02 to look for zeros until we find all of them? It is true that program ZER∅02 would easily find $-2$ as a zero of $f(x) = x^4 + 5x^3 + 9x^2 + 8x + 4$, but then what? Program ZER∅02 will find no further zeros. We may use the results of a run of program DIVIDE to see why.

The output of program DIVIDE above tells us that

$$x^4 + 5x^3 + 9x^2 + 8x + 4 = (x + 2)(x^3 + 3x^2 + 3x + 2)$$

So $-2$ is a zero of our function $f(x) = x^4 + 5x^3 + 9x^2 + 8x + 4$. Next we want a zero of $q(x) = x^3 + 3x^2 + 3x + 2$. Let's use program ZER∅02 to find that zero.

```
890   DATA   3,   1,3,3,2
RUN
ZER002

POLYNOMIAL IS 1   3   3   2

FIRST, LAST, STEP?  -5,5,1


-2 IS A ZERO
```

A run of ZER∅02 with the new data reveals why we could not have found one of the other zeros. We now see that $-2$ is a zero of the function $f$ twice and our program had no way of determining that fact. Values that occur more than once as zeros are called multiple zeros. Why wouldn't ZER∅02 find the other two zeros? Let's divide $q(x)$ by $(x + 2)$ and find out.

```
890   DATA   3,   1,3,3,2
RUN
DIVIDE

P(X)= 1   3   3   2
DIVIDE BY X-?  -2
QUOTIENT  1   1   1 REMAINDER = 0
```

Thus one factored form of our original polynomial is

$$(x + 2)(x + 2)(x^2 + x + 1)$$

The first two factors tell us that $-2$ is a zero twice and analyzing the third factor using the quadratic formula tells us that the final two zeros are nonreal numbers. They are $-\frac{1}{2} + \frac{1}{2}i\sqrt{3}$ and $-\frac{1}{2} - \frac{1}{2}i\sqrt{3}$.

Thus we see that the ability to divide polynomials by $(x - z)$ where $z$ is a zero of the polynomial function makes more information available to us than we would have if we limited ourselves to the procedures of program ZERØ02. The ability to divide enables us to find multiple zeros and, where we are able to divide so that the quotient polynomial is a quadratic, we are able to determine nonreal zeros. We note that caution must be exercised when dividing by approximate zeros. Each succeeding division will be susceptible to additional error.

## Summary of Sec. 8-3

The Factor Theorem tells us that when we find a zero $z$, we may divide the polynomial by $(x - z)$ to obtain a new polynomial with one less zero. Synthetic division has been shown to duplicate the steps of evaluating a polynomial by the nesting method and so enables us to easily perform the division indicated by the results of the factor theorem. This enables us to find multiple zeros and, in some cases, nonreal zeros.

## Problems for Sec. 8-3

1) Write a program to find the zeros of third-degree polynomials by finding the first zero and then finding the remaining zeros by using the quadratic formula.
2) Incorporate synthetic division into program ZERØ02 so that whenever a zero is found, the division is performed and a search is begun for the next zero.
3) Use the methods of this section to find as many zeros as possible for the problems of problem 1 in Sec. 8-2.

## 8-4  Miscellaneous Aids

### Integral Zeros

It can be shown that for an $n$th degree polynomial with zeros $z_n$, $z_{n-1}, \ldots, z_2, z_1$ that the following is true:

$$(x - z_n)(x - z_{n-1}) \ldots (x - z_2)(x - z_1)$$
$$= a_n x^n + a_{n-1} x^{n-1} + \ldots + a_1 x + a_0$$

Considering the product of $n$ binomials on the left we can see that $(-z_n) \cdot (-z_{n-1}) \ldots (-z_2)(-z_1)$ is the constant term in the product which must equal the constant term on the right, or $a_0$. If there is at least one integral zero and $a_0$ is an integer, that means that all integral zeros of a polynomial must be factors of $a_0$. So we could write a program somewhat simpler than ZERØ01 that would search only for integral zeros by first determining all integral factors of $a_0$. In program ZERØ01 we used $p(1)$ for $a_0$.

### Descartes' Rule of Signs

Consider the polynomial $x^2 + 8x + 1$. It should be clear that no matter what positive value we might try for $x$, we can never make $x^2 + 8x + 1$ equal zero because $x^2$ and $8x$ are both positive for $x$ positive. Thus in searching for real zeros we need not consider any positive numbers. The same is true for $-2x^2 - 5x - 1$. Now, what about $x^2 + 3x - 1$? Can there be more than one positive value of $x$ for which $x^2 + 3x - 1 = 0$? No! Consider as another example $x^2 + 1$. There is no positive replacement for $x$ to make $x^2 + 1$ equal to zero, and likewise there is no negative replacement for $x$ that makes $x^2 + 1$ equal to zero since $x^2$ would have to equal $-1$. That tells us that since $x^2 + 1$ is a second-degree polynomial and has two complex zeros, they must both be nonreal. Descartes observed all this and more and left us with Descartes' Rule of Signs.

We may define the variation $v$ in a sequence of numbers as the number of changes in sign found by comparing successive pairs of adjacent numbers. For example, for the sequence 1, 3, 4, $-8$, 2, the value of $v$ is 2. There is no change for 1 to 3 or 3 to 4. There is one change for 4 to $-8$ and for $-8$ to 2. If zeros appear in the sequence, we drop them. The sequence $-2$, 8, 0, 5, $-3$, 6 becomes $-2$, 8, 5, $-3$, 6 in order to determine the number of variations, which is 3.

Descartes' Rule of Signs says that for

$$a_n x^n + a_{n-1} x^{n-1} + \ldots a_1 x + a_0$$

the number of positive zeros depends on the number of variations in the sequence, $a_n$, $a_{n-1}$, $\ldots$, $a_1$, $a_0$, in the following manner. If $v$ is the number of variations, then the number of positive zeros is either $v$ or $v - 2$ or $v - 4$, etc., but not less than zero. This may be written $v - 2i$ where $i$ is a positive integer.

It turns out that we may find a corresponding number for negative zeros by finding positive zeros for $p(-x)$. Substituting $-x$ for $x$ will change the sign of all terms which have an odd exponent for $x$. Thus if $p(x) = -4x^5 - 3x^4 + 5x^3 - 2x^2 + x - 3$, the value of $v$ is 4 and there must be 4 or 2 or 0 positive zeros. Now we find that $p(-x) = +4x^5 - 3x^4 - 5x^3 - 2x^2 - x - 3$ and that $v$ is 1. Thus there must be exactly one negative zero. For example, in $3x^6 - 2x^5 + x^4 - 2x^3 + 5x^2 - x + 1$, we might expect to find as many as six positive zeros, but under no conditions would we look for negative zeros since $p(-x) = 3x^6 + 2x^5 + x^4 + 2x^3 + 5x^2 + 1$, which gives zero variations. All of this gives us a great deal of information. Sometimes the information is exact, as when we get 0 or 1 as the number of variations. At other times we get only a guide, as with $x^3 + 2x^2 + 2x + 1$, which has no positive real zeros and three variations for $p(-x)$, which gives 3 or 1 negative real zeros. A solution of the problem will yield one negative zero and two nonreal zeros in this particular example.

## Problems for Sec. 8-4

1) Write a program to produce polynomials of random degree when zeros are all random integral values.

2) Write a program to produce an $n$th degree polynomial given $n$ integral zeros.

3) Modify program ZERØ01 to find all integral zeros by having $x$ go from $-a_0$ to $a_0$ STEP SGN $(a_0)$.

4) In problem 3, how many additions and multiplications would be required in $a_0 = 100$ for nesting compared to the use of exponents, not counting the loop operations?

5) Modify program ZERØ01 to find all integral zeros by having $x$ take on only values which are factors of $a_0$.

6) Analyze the number of operations called for in problem 5 as compared to problem 3 for selected values of $a_0$.

7) Write a routine to use Descartes' Rule of Signs which merely prints the number of possible zeros in each of the following categories: complex, positive, negative, and zero. Be careful about zero coefficients.

8) Incorporate the routines of problem 7 in ZERØ02 so that the computer stops searching if it has found enough positive zeros and if it has found enough negative zeros. Be sure to have the program check for both positive and negative possibilities.

9) An upper bound may be placed on zeros by finding a non-negative value of $z$ such that after dividing by $(x - z)$, all nonzero terms in the third line of the synthetic division are of the same sign, provided the leading coefficient of $p(x)$ is positive. A lower bound may be found by taking the negative of the upper bound for $p(-x)$. Write a program to find upper and lower bounds.

# SEQUENCES AND SERIES

## 9-1 Sequences

A sequence is simply a list of numbers. It is, of course, a natural for use in computers, although a computer list may not be essential for a particular application.

Sequences come in two kinds, finite and infinite. Obviously we will only be able to evaluate a finite number of terms for any sequence used in a computer.

We routinely work with sequences. The set of counting numbers is a sequence, as is the set of odd integers and the set of even integers. If we were to consider 10 random numbers, they could constitute a sequence. It is more usual that the numbers in a sequence follow some relatively simple pattern. One such sequence you've probably seen goes 1, 1, 2, 3, 5, 8, where every number from the third on is the sum of the previous two. This is called the Fibonacci sequence. The numbers in this sequence have widespread significance in mathematics, art, and nature. We can easily write a program to compute elements of this sequence, store them in a list, and print them, as shown in Program FIBO1. One can generate a Fibonacci type sequence by selecting any two integers for $F(1)$ and $F(2)$.

```
FIBO1

94    REM * THIS PRØGRAM PRINTS THE FIRST
95    REM  30 FIBØNACCI NUMBERS
100   DIM F(30)
102
104   REM * STØRE THE NUMBERS IN A LIST
110   LET F(1) = F(2) = 1
120   FØR X = 3 TØ 30
130      LET F(X) = F(X-1) + F(X-2)
140   NEXT X
142
```

```
144   REM * NØW PRINT THE LIST
150   FØR X = 1 TØ 30
160      PRINT F(X),
170   NEXT X
172
180   END
RUN
FIBOI
```

| | | | | |
|---|---|---|---|---|
| 1 | 1 | 2 | 3 | 5 |
| 8 | 13 | 21 | 34 | 55 |
| 89 | 144 | 233 | 377 | 610 |
| 987 | 1597 | 2584 | 4181 | 6765 |
| 10946 | 17711 | 28657 | 46368 | 75025 |
| 121393 | 196418 | 317811 | 514229 | 832040 |

Probably one of the simplest sequences is the set of counting numbers. It begins 1, 2, 3, . . . . This is an example of an "arithmetic sequence." An arithmetic sequence is one in which we get from one term to the next by adding a constant, called the common difference. The general form for the $n$th term of such a sequence is $t_n = t_1 + (n - 1)d$, and we will discuss this later. For the counting sequence, $d = 1$.

Some sequences are motivated by physical problems. Suppose you are 200 feet from a fixed point. How long will it take to reach that point if you cover half the remaining distance every minute? It should be clear that you cannot ever reach that point, because at every minute along the way there is still a distance separating you from the point and half of that is still a nonzero distance. So there is always a distance remaining, and you can only cover half of it in the next minute. However, it is also clear that at some point you can reach out and touch the point. So we might ask how long it will take to be within six inches. Consider program HALF.

```
HALF

94    REM * THIS PROGRAM HALVES DISTANCE
95
96    REM * INITIAL CONDITIONS - 200 FEET AT TIME ZERO
100   LET D = 200
110   LET T = 0
112
114   REM * NØW COVER HALF THE REMAINING DISTANCE
115   REM   EVERY MINUTE
120   LET T = T+1
130   LET D = D*(1/2)
140      IF D > 6/12 THEN 120
150   PRINT  "DISTANCE ="; D; "FEET"
160   PRINT  "IN"; T; "MINUTES"
170   END
RUN
HALF

DISTANCE = 0.390625 FEET
IN 9 MINUTES
```

If we change HALF to look at the intermediate values of D, we get an example of another common type of sequence. Consider program HALF1.

```
135   PRINT  T; D
RUN
HALF1
```

```
1    100
2    50
3    25
4    12.5
5    6.25
6    3.125
7    1.5625
8    0.78125
9    0.390625
DISTANCE = 0.390625 FEET
IN 9 MINUTES
```

Each term in the sequence is calculated by multiplying the previous term by a constant. In our problem the constant is $\frac{1}{2}$. Such sequences are called "geometric sequences." The constant term is called the "common ratio." The $n$th term of a geometric sequence can be found by the formula $t_n = t_1 r^{(n-1)}$, where $r$ is the common ratio.

A common situation described by a geometric sequence is compound interest. If you put money in a savings account, the bank adds interest to the account at regular intervals, and the amount becomes the principle for the next interest period. If the interest rate per interest period is $r$, we get the amount at the end of that period as $p + pr$, which equals $p(1 + r)$, and at the end of $n$ periods we get $p(1 + r)^n$. If you put \$100 in a bank for one year at 5% interest compounded monthly, the rate for each interest period would be .05/12, and the number of interest periods would be 12. Consider Program INT.

```
INT

94     REM * THIS PRØGRAM CALCULATES CØMPØUND
95     REM  INTEREST BY FØRMULA
100    READ N
110    FØR I = 1 TØ N
120       READ P, R1, N1, Y
130       LET R = R1/N1
140       LET N = N1*Y
150       LET A = P*(1+R/100)↑N
160       PRINT  "$"; P; "AT"; R1; "% FØR"; Y; "YEARS"
170       PRINT  "CØMPØUNDED"; N1; "TIMES ANNUALLY BECØMES $"; A
180       PRINT
190    NEXT I
192
194    REM
200    DATA  3
210    DATA  100, 5, 4, 2
220    DATA  100, 5, 12, 2
230    DATA  100, 5, 365, 2
240    END
RUN
INT

$ 100 AT 5 % FØR 2 YEARS
CØMPØUNDED 4 TIMES ANNUALLY BECØMES $ 110.449

$ 100 AT 5 % FØR 2 YEARS
CØMPØUNDED 12 TIMES ANNUALLY BECØMES $ 110.494

$ 100 AT 5 % FØR 2 YEARS
CØMPØUNDED 365 TIMES ANNUALLY BECØMES $ 110.516
```

For some sequences we are merely given a formula. For example, consider the sequence for which the $n$th term is $(2n - 1)/(2n + 1)$. We see the first 20 terms in program SEQO1.

```
SEQ01

94    REM * THIS PROGRAM PRINTS 20 TERMS OF THE
95    REM   SEQUENCE (2*N-1)/(2*N+1)
100   DEF FNS(N) = (2*N-1) / (2*N+1)
110   FOR I = 1 TO 20
120       PRINT  FNS(I), 2*I-1; "/"; 2*I+1
130   NEXT I
132
140   END
RUN
SEQ01

      0.333333      1 / 3
      0.6           3 / 5
      0.714286      5 / 7
      0.777778      7 / 9
      0.818182      9 / 11
      0.846154     11 / 13
      0.866667     13 / 15
      0.882353     15 / 17
      0.894737     17 / 19
      0.904762     19 / 21
      0.913043     21 / 23
      0.92         23 / 25
      0.925926     25 / 27
      0.931034     27 / 29
      0.935484     29 / 31
      0.939394     31 / 33
      0.942857     33 / 35
      0.945946     35 / 37
      0.948718     37 / 39
      0.95122      39 / 41
```

## Summary of Sec. 9-1

Sequences are defined as lists of numbers. Sequences may be motivated by a study of some natural phenomenon or simply an interest in the relationships of numbers.

## Problems for Sec. 9-I

1) Beginning with the second Fibonacci number, and continuing to the eighteenth term of the sequence find (a) the square of the term, (b) the product of the immediately preceding and the immediately following terms, and (c) the difference of the numbers obtained in (a) and (b).

2) For at least 25 Fibonacci numbers, find, for all possible pairs, the greatest common factor.

3) For at least 15 Fibonacci numbers, print the ratios of adjacent terms.

4) Have the computer print at least 20 elements of a general Fibonacci sequence making $f(1) = 1$ and $f(2) = 3$, or any $f(1)$ and $f(2)$ you prefer.

5) For a general Fibonacci sequence like that in problem 4, print the ratio of adjacent terms.

6) For a general Fibonacci sequence like that in problem 4, print the square of each term from the second to the next to last, the product of the one just before and the one just after, and the difference of these results.

7) Find the accrual to $1000 after seven years at 6% interest compounded monthly and also compounded daily.

8) Find how many minutes it will take for you to get to within six inches of a point if you start 200 feet away and every minute you cover one-third of the remaining distance.

9) Suppose that a rubber ball is known to bounce to three-fourths of the height from which it is dropped. If the ball is dropped from 10 feet, how many bounces will it take to bounce back less than one inch?

10) If you were to place one grain of rice on the first square of a chess board, two grains on the second, four grains on the third, doubling the number from each square to the next, how many grains would you have to place on the 64th square? (Could you?)

11) Print a few terms of any of the following:

    (a) $2n + 3$                     (d) $n^n$

    (b) $2n^2 - n + 1$           (e) $n^{(1/n)}$

    (c) $2^n/n^2$                 (f) $(1 + 1/n)^n$

## 9-2   Convergence and Divergence

Looking at the sequences of the last section and the results of the problems, we can see some differences. Note that for the Fibonacci sequence, the numbers get larger and larger, and for the sequence in which the distance is halved each minute, the terms get closer and closer to zero. For the sequence generated by $(2n - 1)/(2n + 1)$, the terms seem to get closer and closer to one. The later two sequences are examples of converging sequences, and the Fibonacci sequence is an example of a diverging sequence.

If a sequence converges on some value, then that value is called the limit of the sequence. In the formal study of limits, methods are developed for determining whether or not a sequence has a limit and for finding the limit if it does exist. However, we will take a somewhat informal approach here.

The limit of a sequence of values $s_1, s_2, \ldots s_n$ is denoted by

$$\lim_{n \to \infty} s_n$$

Thus for $s_n = (2n - 1)/(2n + 1)$, we write:

$$\lim_{n \to \infty} \frac{2n - 1}{2n + 1} = 1$$

Note that there is no integer for which $(2n - 1)/(2n + 1)$ actually equals one, but the larger $n$ gets, the closer to one the value of $(2n - 1)/(2n + 1)$ becomes. We can get some insight into the behavior of sequences by looking at a few terms, even if that insight is that we need to look at still more terms. In order to be certain about the properties of some sequences, you should pursue a formal study of limits. However, one clear benefit of using the computer is that we may look at hundreds or even thousands of terms without tedious hand calculations. Of course, one way to save computer time is to print only those values that we are interested in seeing. Sequences converge and diverge at vastly different rates. Therefore don't be too quick to infer too much from just a few terms.

We can look at $\lim_{i \to \infty} (-\frac{3}{5})^i$ by writing a very short program to print some terms. See program LIM01.

```
LIM01

94    REM * THIS PRØGRAM PRINTS SAMPLE VALUES
95    REM   FØR THE SEQUENCE S = (-3/5)↑H
100   DEF FNL(H) = (-3/5)↑H
110   FØR I = 1 TØ 10
120      PRINT  I; FNL(I)
130   NEXT I
132
140   PRINT   100; FNL(100)
150   PRINT   101; FNL(101)
160   END
RUN
LIM01

 1  -0.6
 2   0.36
 3  -0.216
 4   0.1296
 5  -0.07776
 6   0.046656
 7  -2.79936E-2
 8   1.67962E-2
 9  -1.00777E-2
 10  6.04662E-3
 100  6.53319E-23
 101 -3.91991E-23
```

Looking at just the first 10 terms we can see that each term is closer to zero than the one before and that the values alternate between positive and negative. For the one-hundredth term, we get $6.5 \times 10^{-23}$ and for the one-hundred and first term we get $-3.9 \times 10^{-23}$, making us more and more confident that the limit is zero.

Not all converging sequences converge on zero. Consider $\lim\limits_{n \to \infty} (2 + \frac{1}{5}^n)$. We can see that $(\frac{1}{5})^n$ converges on zero, and therefore $2 + (\frac{1}{5})^n$ converges on $2 + 0$, or 2. Look at program LIM02, and see how much faster it converges than program LIM01.

```
LIM02

94    REM * THIS PRØGRAM PRINTS SAMPLE VALUES
95    REM   FØR THE SEQUENCE S = (2+(1/5)↑H)
100   DEF FNL(H) = (2+(1/5)↑H)
110   FØR I = 1 TØ 10
120      PRINT I; FNL(I)
130   NEXT I
132
140   END
RUN
LIM02

 1   2.2
 2   2.04
 3   2.008
 4   2.0016
 5   2.00032
 6   2.00006
 7   2.00001
 8   2.
 9   2.
 10  2.
```

It should be clear that if any number $n$ such that $|n| < 1$ is raised to higher and higher powers, the closer to zero $n$ is, the faster the result approaches zero.

We will look at an example of divergence before we leave this section. Suppose that we have a magic ball that bounces to 110 percent of the height from which it is dropped. If we drop this ball from 10 feet, after one bounce it reaches 11 feet. After the second bounce, it reaches 12.1 feet, etc. How high will it go after 10 bounces? See program BØUNCE.

```
BØUNCE

94    REM * THIS PRØGRAM PRINTS HEIGHTS FØR A BALL
95    REM   RECØVERING 110% ØF ITS HEIGHT EACH BØUNCE
100   LET H = 10
110   FØR I = 1 TØ 10
120      LET H = H*1.10
130      PRINT I; H
140   NEXT I
142
150   END
RUN
BØUNCE

1    11
2    12.1
3    13.31
4    14.641
5    16.1051
6    17.7156
7    19.4872
8    21.4359
9    23.5795
10   25.9374
```

## Summary of Sec. 9-2

We have been judging divergence and convergence of sequences by looking at successive terms.

## Problems for Sec. 9-2

1) Compare the convergence of $(-\frac{100}{101})^n$ with $(\frac{1}{10})^n$.

2) Print a few terms of $1 + (\frac{2}{3})^n$ and $(1 + (\frac{2}{3}))^n$.

3) Write a program to give enough terms of $(2 + (n - 2)/n^2)$ to decide on convergence.

4) Write a program to examine any or all of the following:

   (a) $\dfrac{n^2 + 3n - 1}{n}$

   (b) $\dfrac{n - 1}{(n + 1)(n - 2)}$

   (c) $1/n!$

   (d) $1 - 1/3! + 1/5! + \ldots + (-1)^{n+1}/(2n - 1)!$

   (e) $(1 + (1/n)^n)$

   (f) $\dfrac{\sin(n)}{n}$

5) It can be shown for the Fibonacci sequence that the $n$th term is:

$$F_n = \frac{(1 + \sqrt{5})^2 - (1 - \sqrt{5})^2}{2^n\sqrt{5}}$$

Verify this for a reasonable number of terms.

## 9-3 Series

A series is what you get if you write the terms of a sequence with plus signs between them. In other words, a series is the sum of a sequence. Thus the series for the counting sequence is

$$1 + 2 + 3 + 4 + 5 + \cdots$$

The sum of the first five terms is 15. Note that if we look at successive sums, we can form yet another sequence called the sequence of partial sums. For the counting sequence, we get

$$\underbrace{1}_{1}, \underbrace{1 + 2}_{3}, \underbrace{1 + 2 + 3}_{6}, \underbrace{1 + 2 + 3 + 4}_{10}, \underbrace{1 + 2 + 3 + 4 + 5}_{15}, \cdots.$$

We could look at the series associated with that sequence and so on without end.

For some series, we can evaluate the sum by formula, and for others, to do so is difficult. It is even possible to evaluate the sum by formula for certain infinite sequences.

Looking at an arithmetic series of $n$ terms, we see that

$$s_n = t_1 + (t_1 + 1d) + (t_1 + 2d) + \ldots + (t_1 + (n - 1)d) \qquad (8\text{-}1)$$

and looking at the same series in reverse order we see that

$$s_n = (t_1 + (n - 1)d) + \ldots + (t_1 + 2d) + (t_1 + 1d) + t_1 \qquad (8\text{-}2)$$

Adding (8-2) to (8-1) we get

$$2s_n = (2t_1 + (n - 1)d) + \ldots + (2t_1 + (n - 1)d) + (2t_1 + (n - 1)d)$$
$$+ (2t_1 + (n - 1)d)$$

which is therefore twice the sum $s_n$. Note that $2t_1 + (n - 1)d$ occurs $n$ times. Thus we get $2s_n = n(2t_1 + (n - 1)d)$ or $2s_n = n(t_1 + (t_1 + (n - 1)d)$. Since the $n$th term is $t_1 + (n - 1)d$, we get $2s_n = n(t_1 + t_n)$ or

$$s_n = (n/2)(t_1 + t_n)$$

This gives us a choice for finding the sum of an arithmetic series. We may use either the formula, or add terms as we generate them in a computer loop.

For a geometric series we have

$$s_n = t_1 + t_1r + t_1r^2 + \ldots + t_1r^{(n-1)} \qquad (8\text{-}3)$$

Multiplying both sides by $r$ we get

$$rs_n = t_1r + t_1r^2 + t_1r^3 + \ldots + t_1r^n \qquad (8\text{-}4)$$

Subtracting (8-4) from (8-3) we get

$$s_n - rs_n = t_1 - t_1r^n$$

which simplifies to

$$s_n = t_1 \left( \frac{1 - r^n}{1 - r} \right)$$

Again we have the choice of finding the sum by formula or by having the computer add terms as it generates them.

We can get some idea about how the arithmetic and geometric series behave by picking two terms and treating them as the first and second terms for both kinds of sequences. This is done for two pairs of terms in two runs of program GEØARI.

Note that in both cases the sequence of sums for the arithmetic sequence seems to diverge. In fact, all arithmetic sequences for $d <> 0$ diverge and so do their associated sequences of sums. We can see that one of the geometric sequences diverges and the other seems to converge. All geometric sequences and their associated series for which $|r| < 1$ converge.

```
GEØARI

94    REM * THIS PRØGRAM PRINTS VALUES FØR GEØMETRIC AND
95    REM   ARITHMETIC SEQUENCES AND SERIES WITH THE SAME
96    REM   FIRST TWØ TERMS
100   PRINT  "FIRST TWØ TERMS";
110   INPUT A(1), A(2)
120   LET S(1) = T(1) = G(1) = A(1)
130   LET G(2) = A(2)
132
134   REM * FIND CØMMØN DIFFERENCE FØR ARITHMETIC SEQUENCE
140   LET D = A(2) - A(1)
142
144   REM * FIND CØMMØN RATIØ FØR GEOMETRIC SEQUENCE
150   LET R = G(2)/G(1)
160   PRINT  "TERM", "GEØ SEQ", "GEØ SERIES",
170   PRINT  "ARITH SEQ", "ARITH SERIES"
172
174   REM * STØRE SUCCESSIVE VALUES IN LISTS
180   FØR I = 2 TO 10
190      LET G(I) = G(I-1)*R
200      LET S(I) = S(I-1) + G(I)
210      LET A(I) = A(I-1) + D
220      LET T(I) = T(I-1) + A(I)
230   NEXT I
232
234   REM * PRINT RESULTS
240   FØR I = 1 TO 10
250      PRINT  I, G(I), S(I), A(I), T(I)
260   NEXT I
262
270   END


RUN
GEØARI

FIRST TWØ TERMS?1,2
TERM        GEØ SEQ        GEØ SERIES     ARITH SEQ      ARITH SERIES
 1            1              1              1              1
 2            2              3              2              3
 3            4              7              3              6
 4            8             15              4             10
 5           16             31              5             15
 6           32             63              6             21
 7           64            127              7             28
 8          128            255              8             36
 9          256            511              9             45
10          512           1023             10             55
```

```
RUN
GEOARI

FIRST TWO TERMS?4,3
TERM        GEO SEQ      GEO SERIES    ARITH SEQ    ARITH SERIES
  1         4            4             4            4
  2         3            7             3            7
  3         2.25         9.25          2            9
  4         1.6875       10.9375       1            10
  5         1.26562      12.2031       0            10
  6         .949219      13.1523       -1           9
  7         .711914      13.8643       -2           7
  8         .533936      14.3982       -3           4
  9         .400452      14.7986       -4           0
 10         .300339      15.099        -5           -5
```

Looking at the formula for the sum of a geometric sequence,

$$s_n = t_1 \left( \frac{1 - r^n}{1 - r} \right)$$

we can see for $|r| < 1$ that $r^n$ gets closer and closer to zero as $n$ gets larger and larger. Thus $1 - r^n$ gets closer and closer to one, that is, $\lim_{n \to \infty} 1 - r^n = 1$, and

$$\lim_{n \to \infty} s_n = \lim_{n \to \infty} t_1 \left( \frac{1 - r^n}{1 - r} \right) = t_1 \left( \frac{1}{1 - r} \right)$$

Thus for an infinite sequence with $|r| < 1$,

$$s = t_1 \left( \frac{1}{1 - r} \right)$$

Finally, we will look at some other series in the next section.

## Summary of Sec. 9-3

We have defined a series as what we get by replacing commas with plus signs in sequences. We can find the successive sums of a series, which is the sequence of partial sums. For an arithmetic series the $n$th sum is $s_n = (n/2) \cdot (t_1 + t_n)$, and for a geometric series the $n$th sum is $s_n = t_1 (1 - r^n)/(1 - r)$.

Series either converge on some real number value or they diverge. All arithmetic series diverge, and geometric series diverge for a common ratio greater than or equal to 1 or less than or equal to $-1$.

## Problems for Sec. 9-3

1) For the magic ball bounding to 110 percent of its height in Sec. 9-2, find the total distance traveled before reaching the height of the tenth bounce.
2) Find the sum of the first $n$ positive integers for the following values of $n$: 10, 100, 1000, and 10000.
3) In the song "The Twelve Days of Christmas," gifts are bestowed upon the singer in the following pattern: the first day she receives a partridge in a pear tree; the second day two turtle doves and a partridge in a pear

tree; the third day three French hens, two turtle doves, and a partridge in a pear tree. This continues for 12 days. On the twelfth day she receives $12 + 11 + \cdots + 2 + 1$ gifts. How many gifts were there altogether? Note that the figure asked for here is the twelfth term of the sequence of partial sums of the sequence of partial sums of the sequence of positive integers.

## 9-4 More on Series

There are many series that have importance in the field of mathematics which are neither arithmetic nor geometric.

It can be shown that the cosine is the sum of an infinite sequence:

$$\cos(x) = 1 - \frac{x^2}{2!} + \frac{x^4}{4!} - \cdots + (-1)^{n+1} \frac{x^{2n-2}}{(2n-2)!} + \cdots$$

While this is a very tedious calculation by hand, it is relatively simple with the aid of a computer program. As with finding zeros for polynomials, we use a relative comparison to decide when to stop (see line 180 of program CØSINE). However, in the case of polynomial evaluation, we were using the value at the midpoint of an interval which we knew contained the true value. In that case we had a measure of relative error. In the present situation we have somewhat less information. We have only the sum of $n$ terms to compare with the sum of $n - 1$ terms. Thus we are saying that the magnitude of the most recent term is small enough to stop summing. When the magnitude of the most recent term is very small compared to the sum so far, we may expect the error to be small also, but not necessarily as small. We have not attempted to measure the cumulative effect of the remaining terms, although methods exist for evaluating it.

```
CØSINE

 94    REM * THIS PRØGRAM APPRØXIMATES CØSINE X
 95    REM  USING TERMS ØF A SERIES
100    PRINT  "FIND CØSINE ØF";
110    INPUT X
120    LET S1 = S = N = F = 1
130    PRINT  N; S
140    LET N = N+1
150    LET S1 = S
152
154    REM * F IS THE VALUE ØF FACTORIAL 2*N-2
160    LET F = F*( 2*N-2 )*( 2*N-3 )
170    LET S = S + ((-1)↑(N+1) * X↑( 2*N-2 )/F )
180       IF ABS(S-S1)/(ABS(S)+ABS(S1)) > 1E-6 THEN 130
190    PRINT  "BY CØMPUTER CØSINE FUNCTIØN"; CØS(X)
200    END
RUN
CØSINE

FIND CØSINE ØF? 1.57
 1   1
 2  -0.23245
 3   2.07055E-2
 4  -9.45914E-5
 5   8.20947E-4
 6   7.95873E-4
 7   7.96341E-4
 8   7.96335E-4
BY CØMPUTER CØSINE FUNCTIØN 7.96334E-4
```

Similarly it can be shown that

$$\sin(x) = x - \frac{x^3}{3!} + \frac{x^5}{5!} - \ldots + (-1)^{n+1} \frac{x^{2n-1}}{(2n-1)!}$$

Evaluation of this is left as a problem.

## Problems for Sec. 9-4

1) Write a program to calculate $\sin(x)$ using the series in this section.
2) Each of the following series approaches pi as $n$ increases.

   (a) $4\left(1 - \frac{1}{3} + \frac{1}{5} - \ldots + (-1)^{n-1}\frac{1}{(2n-1)} + \ldots\right)$

   (b) $6\left(\frac{1}{1^2} + \frac{1}{2^2} + \ldots + \frac{1}{n^2}\right)$

   (c) $8\left(\frac{1}{1^2} + \frac{1}{3^2} + \ldots + \frac{1}{(2n-1)^2}\right)$

   Write a program to compare convergence for each of the above.

3) The constant $e$, whose value is approximately 2.718, is of importance in calculus. It can be shown that

   $$\frac{1}{0!} + \frac{1}{1!} + \frac{1}{2!} + \ldots + \frac{1}{n!}$$

   and

   $$\left(1 + \frac{1}{n}\right)^n$$

   both approach $e$ as $n$ increases. Compare convergence for the two different methods of calculating $e$.

4) One method of approximating pi is to select random points in a square and find how many of them fall within a quarter circle whose radius is a side of the square. The number of points that fall within the quarter circle should be proportional to the area. The area of the quarter circle is $\frac{1}{4}\pi r^2$, whereas the area of the square is $r^2$. Thus four times the ratio of circle to square should approximate pi. This is a variation of the Monte Carlo method. Write a program to select from 1,000 to 10,000 such points to obtain an approximate value for pi.

# 10
# MATRICES

## 10-1 Introduction

A matrix is simply a rectangular array of numbers. As such, an array is a set of numbers arranged in rows and columns. This is, of course, exactly the array we have been using whenever we have used subscripted numeric variables in BASIC. A matrix may also consist of a single row or a single column. Such arrays are sometimes called "row vectors" and "column vectors."

It is the purpose of this chapter to study some of the properties of matrices and see some applications. We will not concern ourselves with theorems and their proofs. A brief review of Sec. 1-5 at this time might be helpful.

Matrices may be studied in a totally abstract setting, but it is useful to have a concrete example. Suppose that we are operating the Framis Corporation, which employs three salesmen (it could be 300): Brown, Jones, and Smith. Brown, Jones, and Smith are selling clevises, hammer handles, shoehorns, and whipsockets. In a given week the three salesmen turn in orders for merchandise as shown in Table 10-1a.

One fundamental piece of information is the amount of money brought in by each salesman. To calculate that we need the prices as shown in Table 10-1b. We can find subtotals by multiplying the price of an item by the number of items. The subtotals are shown in Table 10-2a. Now to obtain each salesman's total, we simply add across the rows to get the figures shown in Table 10-2b.

### TABLE 10-1a ARRAY S

| Salesman | Clevis | Hammer handle | Shoehorn | Whipsocket |
|----------|--------|--------|----------|------------|
| Brown    | 30     | 800    | 50       | 20         |
| Jones    | 50     | 31     | 40       | 10         |
| Smith    | 0      | 500    | 50       | 90         |

**TABLE 10-2a**

| Salesman | Clevis | Hammer handle | Shoehorn | Whipsocket |
|---|---|---|---|---|
| Brown | $30 | $312.00 | $24.50 | $ 75.80 |
| Jones | 50 | 12.08 | 19.60 | 37.90 |
| Smith | 0 | 195.00 | 24.50 | 341.10 |

**TABLE 10-1b ARRAY P**

| Item | Price |
|---|---|
| Clevis | $1.00 |
| Hammer handle | 0.39 |
| Shoehorn | 0.49 |
| Whipsocket | 3.79 |

**TABLE 10-2b ARRAY M**

| Salesman | Dollar sales |
|---|---|
| Brown | $442.30 |
| Jones | 119.59 |
| Smith | 560.60 |

To make the discussion easier, we label the array of Table 10-1a as S, the array of Table 10-1b as P, and the array of Table 10-2b as M. Thus to get $M(1,1)$, we add the products $S(1,I)*P(I,1)$, for I going from one to four, and to get $M(2,1)$, we sum the products $S(2,I)*P(I,1)$, for I going from one to four. That makes $M(J,1)$ the sum of the products $S(J,I)*P(I,1)$ for J going from one to three and for I going from one to four. If the P array had had a second column, such as the salesmen's commission per item, we could carry out the above process for the second column, getting $M(J,K)$ by summing up the products $S(J,I)*P(I,K)$, for K going from one to the number of columns in P, J going from one to the number of rows in S, and I going from one to the number of columns in S. Note that the number of columns in S must equal the number of rows in P and that the product array has the number of rows in S and the number of columns in P. This is exactly the definition for matrix multiplication. Therefore, instead of constructing triply-nested loops to perform the algorithm described above, we take advantage of the BASIC matrix multiplication statement (see line 290 of program SALES1). To make the run of the program more readable, we have used string lists to provide labeling.

```
SALES1

94     REM * THIS PRØGRAM CALCULATES SALES TØTALS
95     REM  USING MATRICES
100    DIM S(3,4), P(4,1), M(3,1), I$(4), S$(3)
110    MAT  READ S, P, I$, S$
112
114    REM * PRINT RAW DATA IN LINES 120 THRØUGH 260
120    PRINT  "SALESMAN\ITEM",
130    FØR I = 1 TØ 4
140       PRINT I$(I),
150    NEXT I
152
160    FØR I = 1 TØ 3
170       PRINT S$(I),
180       FØR J = 1 TØ 4
```

```
190          PRINT  S(I,J),
200       NEXT  J
202
210    NEXT  I
220    PRINT
222
230    PRINT  "ITEM",  "PRICE"
240    FØR  I = 1  TØ  4
250        PRINT  I$(I),  P(I,1)
260    NEXT  I
270    PRINT
272
274    REM * CALCULATE  TØTALS  IN  LINE  290
280    PRINT  "SALESMAN",  "DØLLAR  SALES"
282
290    MAT  M = S*P
300    FØR  I = 1  TØ  3
310        PRINT  S$(I),  M(I,1)
320    NEXT  I
322
324    REM
330    DATA   30,  800,  50,  20
340    DATA   50,  31,  40,  10
350    DATA   0,  500,  50,  90
352
360    DATA   1,  .39,  .49,  3.79
362
370    DATA   CLEVIS,  HAMMER  HANDLE
380    DATA   SHØE  HØRN,  WHIPSØCKET
382
390    DATA   BRØWN,  JØNES,  SMITH
400    END
RUN
SALES1
```

| SALESMAN\ITEM | CLEVIS | HAMMER HANDLE | SHØE HØRN | WHIPSØCKET |
|---|---|---|---|---|
| BRØWN | 30 | 800 | 50 | 20 |
| JØNES | 50 | 31 | 40 | 10 |
| SMITH | 0 | 500 | 50 | 90 |

| ITEM | PRICE |
|---|---|
| CLEVIS | 1 |
| HAMMER HANDLE | 0.39 |
| SHØE HØRN | 0.49 |
| WHIPSØCKET | 3.79 |

| SALESMAN | DØLLAR SALES |
|---|---|
| BRØWN | 442.3 |
| JØNES | 119.59 |
| SMITH | 560.6 |

It may strike you that SALES1 is rather long, and indeed it is. However, most of the program is devoted to producing nicely formatted output. If all that is required is the three dollar amounts at the end of the printout, that can be done with an extremely short program having just one calculation statement and one print statement, as shown in program SALES2.

```
SALES2

100    DIM  S(3,4),  P(4,1),  M(3,1)
110    MAT   READ  S,  P
290    MAT  M = S*P
310    MAT   PRINT  M
330    DATA   30,  800,  50,  20
340    DATA   50,  31,  40,  10
350    DATA   0,  500,  50,  90
```

```
360    DATA    1,  .39,  .49,  3.79
400    END
RUN
SALES2


442.3
119.59
560.6
```

There are many properties of matrices which come to light through the process of just experimenting with different relationships. So it is recommended that you do as many problems as possible and that you work on problems of your own throughout this chapter.

## Summary of Sec. 10-1

Matrices are not only convenient as storage areas for data, they possess mathematical properties that are both interesting and of practical value. The mathematics of matrix algebra is fairly complex, containing numerous abstract, involved, and intricate theorems. The thrust of our work will be to use familiar properties to develop new facts.

## Problems for Sec. 10-1

1) As manager of the Framis Corporation of this section, you are interested only in total sales. Create a row vector T to contain the sales totals by item for the week. Then find T*P and print it.

2) MAT READ the integers 1 through 12 into both a column vector C and a row vector R. Find R*C and C*R and print them both.

3) Write a program to print integer powers of an array. How must the number of rows and columns be related for this?

4) A light fixture manufacturer makes three different fixtures requiring parts as shown in the table and wishes to make 800 of fixture A, 200 of fixture B, and 1,500 of fixture C. Write a program to find how many bulbs, switches, meters of wire, and screws will be needed.

|                | A  | B | C  |
|----------------|----|---|----|
| Bulbs          | 3  | 1 | 4  |
| Switches       | 1  | 1 | 2  |
| Meters of wire | 9  | 2 | 3  |
| Screws         | 15 | 8 | 12 |

5) Find any or all of the following products:

$$\text{(a)} \begin{bmatrix} 1 & 0 & 0 \\ 1 & 0 & 0 \\ 1 & 0 & 0 \end{bmatrix} \cdot \begin{bmatrix} 1 & 2 & 3 \\ 4 & 5 & 6 \\ 7 & 8 & 9 \end{bmatrix} \quad \text{(b)} \begin{bmatrix} 0 & 1 & 0 \\ 0 & 1 & 0 \\ 0 & 1 & 0 \end{bmatrix} \cdot \begin{bmatrix} 1 & 2 & 3 \\ 4 & 5 & 6 \\ 7 & 8 & 9 \end{bmatrix}$$

(c) $\begin{bmatrix} 1 & 0 & 0 \\ 0 & 1 & 0 \\ 0 & 0 & 1 \end{bmatrix} \cdot \begin{bmatrix} 1 & 2 & 3 \\ 4 & 5 & 6 \\ 7 & 8 & 9 \end{bmatrix}$

6) Find the result:

$$\begin{bmatrix} [1 & 1 & 1] \end{bmatrix} \cdot \begin{bmatrix} 30 & 800 & 50 & 20 \\ 50 & 31 & 40 & 10 \\ 0 & 500 & 50 & 90 \end{bmatrix} \cdot \begin{bmatrix} 1.00 \\ .39 \\ .49 \\ 3.79 \end{bmatrix}$$

and compare with the results of problem 1.

## 10-2 Solving Simultaneous Linear Equations Using *MAT INV*

The matrix equation,

$$\begin{bmatrix} a_1 & b_1 & c_1 \\ a_2 & b_2 & c_2 \\ a_3 & b_3 & c_3 \end{bmatrix} \cdot \begin{bmatrix} x \\ y \\ z \end{bmatrix} = \begin{bmatrix} d_1 \\ d_2 \\ d_3 \end{bmatrix} \qquad (10\text{-}1)$$

can be multiplied out on the left side to obtain

$$\begin{bmatrix} a_1 x + b_1 y + c_1 z \\ a_2 x + b_2 y + c_2 z \\ a_3 x + b_3 y + c_3 z \end{bmatrix} = \begin{bmatrix} d_1 \\ d_2 \\ d_3 \end{bmatrix} \qquad (10\text{-}2)$$

We say that two matrices are equal if each entry of one equals the corresponding entry of the other. (Each entry of a matrix is often referred to as an element of the matrix.) For MAT A = MAT B that means $A(I,J) = B(I,J)$ for all values of I and J. Therefore, we may say that

$$a_1 x + b_1 y + c_1 z = d_1$$
$$a_2 x + b_2 y + c_2 z = d_2 \qquad (10\text{-}3)$$
$$a_3 x + b_3 y + c_3 z = d_3$$

Equation (10-3) constitutes a system of three linear equations in three un-knowns. Actually Eqs. (10-1), (10-2), and (10-3) are simply three different ways of writing the same equality.

We want to solve the set of equations (10-3). It will be easier to discuss the solution if we assign variables to the matrices of Eq. (10-1) as follows:

$$C = \begin{bmatrix} a_1 & b_1 & c_1 \\ a_2 & b_2 & c_2 \\ a_3 & b_3 & c_3 \end{bmatrix} \qquad S = \begin{bmatrix} x \\ y \\ z \end{bmatrix} \qquad K = \begin{bmatrix} d_1 \\ d_2 \\ d_3 \end{bmatrix}$$

Matrix C may be referred to as the coefficient matrix, S the solution matrix, and K the matrix of constants. Now we may rewrite Eq. (10-1) in the form

$$C*S = K \qquad (10\text{-}4)$$

and proceed to solve for S.

It would be very convenient if we could just divide both sides by C. But it turns out that the division of one matrix by another is not an easily describable process. However, division by C is equivalent to multiplication by the inverse of C and the inverse of C, if it exists, is easily obtained in BASIC.

Before we use an inverse to solve simultaneous linear equations let's look more closely at just what the inverse of a matrix is. The inverse of a matrix C is the matrix $C^{-1}$ such that the product of C and $C^{-1}$ is the identity matrix. The identity matrix has the same number of rows as columns and is filled with zeros except for the upper left to lower right diagonal, which is filled with ones. Note that in order for a matrix to have an inverse, it must be square.

Let's find, for example, the inverse of

$$\begin{bmatrix} 5 & 6 \\ 7 & 8 \end{bmatrix}$$

We are looking for a matrix with entries a, b, c, and d such that

$$\begin{bmatrix} a & b \\ c & d \end{bmatrix} \cdot \begin{bmatrix} 5 & 6 \\ 7 & 8 \end{bmatrix} = \begin{bmatrix} 1 & 0 \\ 0 & 1 \end{bmatrix}$$

Finding the product on the left we get

$$\begin{bmatrix} 5a + 7b & 6a + 8b \\ 5c + 7d & 6c + 8d \end{bmatrix} = \begin{bmatrix} 1 & 0 \\ 0 & 1 \end{bmatrix}$$

If two matrices are equal, then their corresponding entries are equal. So we get the following four equations with four unknowns:

$$5a + 7b = 1 \qquad 6a + 8b = 0$$

$$5c + 7d = 0 \qquad 6c + 8d = 1$$

We can easily solve these equations to get $a = -4$, $b = 3$, $c = 3.5$, and $d = -2.5$. Therefore,

$$\begin{bmatrix} -4 & 3 \\ 3.5 & -2.5 \end{bmatrix} \cdot \begin{bmatrix} 5 & 6 \\ 7 & 8 \end{bmatrix} = \begin{bmatrix} 1 & 0 \\ 0 & 1 \end{bmatrix}$$

or

$$\begin{bmatrix} 5 & 6 \\ 7 & 8 \end{bmatrix}^{-1} = \begin{bmatrix} -4 & 3 \\ 3.5 & -2.5 \end{bmatrix}$$

We can easily verify this with the demonstration program MATINV. (Note that the computer in some cases, unlike our example here, is susceptible to slight roundoff errors when the MAT INV statement is used.)

Now to get back to solving simultaneous linear equations. We had the

```
MATINV

94    REM * THIS IS A PROGRAM TO DEMONSTRATE MAT INV
100   DIM X(2,2), A(2,2), P(2,2)
110   MAT   READ A
120   MAT X = INV(A)
122
130   PRINT "ORIGINAL MATRIX"
140   MAT   PRINT A
150   PRINT
152
160   PRINT "INVERSE MATRIX"
170   MAT   PRINT X
180   PRINT
182
190   PRINT "THE PRODUCT IS"
200   MAT P = X*A
210   MAT   PRINT P
212
214   REM
220   DATA  5,6, 7,8
230   END
RUN
MATINV

ORIGINAL MATRIX

5              6
7              8

INVERSE MATRIX

-4             3
3.5           -2.5

THE PRODUCT IS

1              0
0              1
```

matrix equation, C * S = K.  Now

$$C^{-1}*C*S = C^{-1}*K \qquad (10\text{-}5)$$

and a matrix times its inverse gives the identity matrix, sometimes designated I.
Thus $C^{-1}*C$ = I.  The identity matrix has the property that for any matrix M
with dimensions compatible with the dimensions of I,

$$I*M = M*I = M$$

Thus Eq. (10-5) becomes

$$I*S = C^{-1}*K$$

or

$$S = C^{-1}*K$$

and we have solved Eq. (10-4) for S, which was our purpose.  It is now a relatively
simple matter to write a program (see program SOLVE) to solve the system,

$$x + 2y - z = 2$$
$$3x - 3y + 2z = 3 \qquad (10\text{-}6)$$
$$4x - y + 2z = 8$$

```
SØLVE

94    REM * THIS PRØGRAM SØLVES SIMULTANEØUS LINEAR
95    REM  EQUATIØNS USING THE MAT INV STATEMENT
100   DIM  C(3,3), S(3,1), K(3,1), N(3,3)
110   MAT  READ C, K
120   MAT N = INV(C)
130   MAT S = N*K
140   PRINT  "SØLUTIØNS:"
150   MAT  PRINT S
152
154   REM
160   DATA  1,2,-1, 3,-3,2, 4,-1,2
170   DATA  2,3,8
180   END
RUN
SØLVE

SØLUTIØNS:

1.
2.
3.
```

In program SØLVE, the column vector,

$$S = \begin{bmatrix} 1 \\ 2 \\ 3 \end{bmatrix}$$

translates back to $x = 1$, $y = 2$, and $z = 3$. We may now substitute these values in Eq. (10-6) to verify that they do in fact solve the system of equations.

### Summary of Sec. 10-2

We have seen that sets of simultaneous linear equations may be solved by considering an equivalent matrix equation C*S = K, where C is the coefficient matrix, S is a column vector which contains the values of the variables in the original set of linear equations, and K is a column vector containing the constant terms in the original set of linear equations. We may solve for S by finding the inverse of matrix C, so that $S = C^{-1}*K$. The inverse may be found with the BASIC statement MAT I = INV(C). For systems of simultaneous linear equations having a unique solution, MAT C will always be square, which is one of the requirements for having an inverse.

### Problems for Sec. 10-2

1) Let

$$A = \begin{bmatrix} 4 & -4 & 4 \\ 1 & 1 & 7 \\ -3 & 9 & -8 \end{bmatrix}$$

Find the print $A^{-1}$, $A*A^{-1}$, and $A^{-1}*A$.

2) Let

$$B = \begin{bmatrix} -8 & -3 \\ 0 & -1 \end{bmatrix}$$

Find $B^{-1}$ and print it.  Verify by hand-computing the inverse of B.
Find and print $B*B^{-1}$ and $B^{-1}*B$.

3) Solve for $x$ and $y$:

$$-2x - 5y = -16$$
$$- x + 4y = 31$$

4) Solve for $x$, $y$, and $z$:

$$2x - 9y - 5z = 2$$
$$7x - 6y + 5z = -35$$
$$9x - 6y + 5z = -39$$

5) Solve for $x$, $y$, and $z$:

$$3x + 4y + z = 7$$
$$5x - 6y + 3z = 8$$
$$3x + 4y + z = -3$$

6) Solve for $w$, $x$, $y$, and $z$:

$$6w + 3x + 6y + 5z = -12$$
$$-7w + 5x - 7y - z = 77$$
$$-3w + x + 3y + 6z = 31$$
$$-2w - 4x + 4y - 7z = -76$$

7) Solve for $w$, $x$, $y$, and $z$:

$$-3w + 6x - 5y - z = -32$$
$$w + 9x - 5y - 2z = 9$$
$$w + 6y + 5z = 2$$
$$-7w + 4x - y + 5z = -86$$

8) Solve for $x$, $y$, and $z$:

$$2x + 4y - 3z = -11.9$$
$$-9x - 3y = 58.5$$
$$-9x + 8y + 5z = 66.6$$

9) Solve for $v$, $w$, $x$, $y$, and $z$:

$$7v + 6w - 3x - y + 9z = 26.3$$
$$-9v + 2w + 9x + 5y + z = 91.1$$
$$-3v + 4w + 5x + 5z = 62.9$$
$$6v - 8x - 2y - 6z = -55.6$$
$$-3v - 9w + 5x + 7y + 3z = -25.9$$

10) Let

$$A = \begin{bmatrix} 1 & -2 & 3 \\ 5 & -1 & -2 \\ 0 & 3 & 4 \end{bmatrix} \text{ and } B = \begin{bmatrix} 2 & -4 & 0 \\ -3 & 1 & 2 \\ 5 & 2 & -5 \end{bmatrix}$$

Find and print $(A*B)^{-1}$ and $B^{-1}*A^{-1}$

11) Write a program that can solve sets of simultaneous linear equations having different numbers of equations. Provide an item of data that is the number of equations and redimension all matrices accordingly.

# 11
# SOME TOPICS
# OF STATISTICS

## 11-1  Introduction

The possibilities for using the computer to analyze and summarize large amounts of data are virtually unlimited. This chapter will introduce just a few fundamental statistical calculations.

## 11-2  Average, Variance, and Standard Deviation

One of the most common measures of statistical information is the average or arithmetic mean. The average is the sum of the measures divided by the number of measures. In some cases the mere task of counting the number of measurements may be a job in itself. So we can even use the computer to do the counting for us. All that is necessary is to append an item of artificial data as a flag to stop counting and calculate the average, as shown in program AVG.

```
AVG

 94   REM * THIS PROGRAM COUNTS DATA AND
 95   REM   CALCULATES AVERAGE
100   LET N = T = 0
110   READ D
120     IF  D = .01 THEN 160
130   LET N = N+1
140   LET T = T+D
150   GOTO 110
160   PRINT  "    MEASUREMENTS"; N
170   LET A = T/N
190   PRINT  "AVERAGE MEASURE"; A
492
494   REM
500   DATA  98, 80, 73, 92, 77, 84, 83, 79, 87, 73
510   DATA  99, 63, 63, 92, 81, 93, 47, 53, 89, 100
520   DATA  98, 71, 73, .01
530   END
```

```
RUN
AVG

MEASUREMENTS 23
AVERAGE MEASURE 80.3478
```

The average for a set of data gives no idea of the spread or dispersion of the data. The average of zero and 100 is 50, and the average of 49 and 51 is also 50. We could get some idea by having the computer find for us the largest and the smallest measures. Even that information could be misleading, since the largest measure could be much larger than the next largest, or the smallest could be much smaller than the next smallest. One way to gain some insight into the distribution of the measures is to find the average of the amount by which each measurement differs or deviates from the average of the measures. There is a flaw here, however, as some will deviate by a positive amount and some will deviate by a negative amount, thus cancelling each other out. Using mean absolute deviation would avoid this difficulty. However, expressions involving absolute value are difficult to work with algebraically, and statisticians thus find the average of the squares of the deviations. This figure is called the "sample variance." In order to write a formula for variance, we use the Greek letter sigma, $\sum$, which indicates summation. Defining average using summation notation looks like this:

$$A = \frac{\sum\limits_{i=1}^{n} x_i}{n}$$

The average $A$ is the sum of all values of $x_i$ for $i$ going from 1 to the number of measurements, which is $n$, divided by the number of measurements. We define variance in terms of the average as follows:

$$V = \frac{\sum\limits_{i=1}^{n} (x_i - A)^2}{n}$$

Even the variance, which gives an indication of how measurements are distributed, doesn't indicate actual dispersion. It indicates the square of dispersion. Thus we take the square root of $V$, getting a number called "standard deviation":

$$S^2 = \frac{\sum\limits_{i=1}^{n} (x_i - A)^2}{n}$$

and

$$S = \sqrt{\frac{\sum\limits_{i=1}^{n} (x_i - A)^2}{n}}$$

Now if we try to apply a computer program directly to the formula for $S^2$, we soon find that we will have to READ the DATA twice, once to find the average, and again to get each value of $x_i - A$. This is not a problem for small amounts of data, but since it can be avoided, let's do so.

It can be shown that

$$\frac{\sum_{i=1}^{n} (x_i - A)^2}{n} = \frac{1}{n} \sum_{i=1}^{n} x_i^2 - A^2$$

This means that we can, alternatively, have the computer sum up the squares of the measures rather than the squares of the deviations. This can easily be incorporated into program AVG. See lines 150 and 210 of program VAR.

```
VAR

94    REM * THIS PRØGRAM CØUNTS DATA AND CALCULATES
95    REM   THE AVERAGE, VARIANCE AND STANDARD DEVIATIØN
100   LET N = T = T1 = 0
110   READ D
120       IF D = .01 THEN 170
130   LET N = N+1
140   LET T = T+D
→150  LET T1 = T1 + D↑2
160   GØTØ 110
170   PRINT "      MEASUREMENTS"; N
172
180   LET A = T/N
190   PRINT "    AVERAGE MEASURE"; A
192
200   LET A1 = T1/N
→210  LET V = A1 - A↑2
220   PRINT "           VARIANCE"; V
222
230   LET S = SQR(V)
240   PRINT "STANDARD DEVIATIØN"; S
492
494   REM
500   DATA  98, 80, 73, 92, 77, 84, 83, 79, 87, 73
510   DATA  99, 63, 63, 92, 81, 93, 47, 53, 89, 100
520   DATA  98, 71, 73, .01
530   END
RUN
VAR

      MEASUREMENTS 23
   AVERAGE MEASURE 80.3478
          VARIANCE 202.314
STANDARD DEVIATIØN 14.2237
```

## Summary of Sec. 11-2

In this section, the average, or arithmetic mean, variance, and standard deviation have all been defined. We have written programs to calculate the average and standard deviation.

## Problems for Sec. 11-2

1) Modify program AVG so that the computer tells us the highest and the lowest measures.

2) Modify program VAR so that we get the deviations of the largest and smallest measures from average in terms of the number of standard deviations. (If the largest measure is 91 for an average of 70 and the standard deviation is 7, then the largest measure would be three standard deviations from average.)

3) Often in practice we use what is called the "weighted average." Suppose that tests count three quizzes and that the final exam counts two tests. Find the weighted average for quiz marks 70, 80, and 73, test marks 63, 82, and 91, and a final exam of 83.

4) Generate 100 random numbers from 1 to 201. Calculate the average and standard deviation.

5) Generate 100 random numbers from -100 to 100 and calculate the average and standard deviation.

6) Devise a scheme without reading data twice for finding accurately the average and standard deviation for the following data: 9999.12, 9999.36, 9999.64, 10000.03, 10000.41, 9999.83, 9999.51, 9999.13 and 10000.08. Due to roundoff error, many programs will give a large standard deviation for the above data. (Hint: we can simply measure differences from 10000 instead of from zero.)

## 11-3   Median

The median is the middle value. Sometimes the median is presented as an item of statistical information, such as median income or median weight. If there are an even number of data items, then the median is the average of the middle two values. One reason for using the median is that it tends to be less affected by a few widely dispersed items of data than the average. There are no particularly difficult calculations required to find the median. What does have to be done, though, is to first arrange the data in numerical order. Thus let us develop an ordering routine.

There are many, many ways of ordering. Some ordering procedures are very elaborate and some are very simple. As the number of items to be sorted increases, the need for efficiency increases. The study of sorting is a fascinating and intriguing one. However, we hesitate to become too involved at this time. We will instead develop an ordering routine that works with only a little attention to efficiency and defer a more sophisticated study of ordering for another time and place.

If we test every adjacent pair of numbers in a list and find that they are in order, then we know that the entire list is in order. This is called a "bubble sort." If we find any adjacent pair that is not in order, then we can direct the computer to exchange those two elements so that they are in order. If every time that we make such an exchange, we turn a switch on by letting $S = 1$, then we can determine at the end of checking through the list that an exchange has been made and that the list might not be in order yet. If after scanning the entire list we find that switch S is still zero, then we know that no exchange has been made and the list must be in order. After the first scan through the list, we know that the number at the end of the list is the highest or lowest depending on which order we specify. That is, it is the number that will be there when the list is finally ordered. Thus we do not need to check the entire list the next time; we can check one less item. See program ∅RDER.

ØRDER

```
94    REM * THIS PRØGRAM ØRDERS UP TØ 200 NUMBERS
100   DIM L(200)
102
104   REM * READ AND CØUNT DATA
110   LET I = 0
120   LET I = I+1
130      IF I <= 200 THEN 160
140   PRINT "CURRENT LIMIT IS 200 NUMBERS"
150   STØP
160   READ L(I)
170      IF L(I) <> .01 THEN 120
180   LET N = I = I-1
184   REM * TURN SWITCH ØFF AND BEGIN SØRT
190   LET S = 0
200   LET N = N-1
210   FØR J = 1 TØ N
220         IF L(J) >= L(J+1) THEN 270
222
224      REM * EXCHANGE ELEMENTS AND TURN SWITCH ØN
230         LET S1 = L(J)
240         LET L(J) = L(J+1)
250         LET L(J+1) = S1
260         LET S = 1
270   NEXT J
272
274   REM * CHECK SWITCH
275   REM   S = 0   SØRT CØMPLETE
276   REM   S = 1   SØRT NØT CØMPLETE
280      IF S = 1 THEN 190
282
284   REM * THE LIST IS IN ØRDER - PRINT IT
290   FØR X = 1 TØ I
300      PRINT L(X);
310   NEXT X
492
494   REM
500   DATA  98, 80, 73, 92, 77, 84, 83, 79, 87, 73
510   DATA  99, 63, 63, 92, 81, 93, 47, 53, 89, 100
520   DATA  98, 71, 73, .01
530   END
RUN
ØRDER
```

```
100  99  98  98  93  92  92  89  87  84  83  81  80  79  77  73  73  73
71  63  63  53  47
```

Note that in line 220 we check for greater than or equal to. What would happen if we only checked for greater than? If there are two equal numbers in the list, the switch will always get turned on and cause the routine to be repeated endlessly. In program ØRDER we have done two things in the interest of efficiency. We do not scan that part of the list that we know to be in order, and we quit when we know the entire list is in order.

There are other things that may be done to improve the efficiency of program ØRDER. One is to sort "up" the list as well as "down." However, in spite of these precautions, the general procedure here is satisfactory only for relatively small amounts of data. If we are to order thousands or hundreds of thousands of data items, then there are far more efficient algorithms which we would have to use. The fundamental weakness in the procedure we have used is that on each pass the computer checks only one less pair of data items than on the previous pass. Much can be gained by partitioning the data to be ordered in such a way that only a small fraction of the data need be scanned each time an item is placed in its final spot in the list. However, such procedures generally require much more programming effort.

If all we want is the median, then there is no need to actually print the data in order. The middle number for I odd is L(INT(I/2)+1) or L(INT((I+1)/2)). See line 320 of program MEDIAN.

```
MEDIAN

94    REM * THIS PROGRAM FINDS THE MEDIAN FOR
95    REM  AN ODD NUMBER OF DATA ITEMS
100   DIM L(200)
110   LET I = 0
120   LET I = I+1
130       IF I <= 200 THEN 160
140   PRINT   "CURRENT LIMIT IS 200 NUMBERS"
150   STOP
160   READ L(I)
170       IF L(I) <> .01 THEN 120
180   LET N = I = I-1
190       IF N/2 <> INT(N/2) THEN 220
200   PRINT   "N EVEN"
210   STOP
220   LET S = 0
230   LET N = N-1
240   FOR J = 1 TO N
250       IF L(J) >= L(J+1) THEN 300
260       LET S1 = L(J)
270       LET L(J) = L(J+1)
280       LET L(J+1) = S1
290       LET S = 1
300   NEXT J
310       IF S = 1 THEN 220
312
→ 320   PRINT   "MEDIAN"; L( INT((I+1)/2) )
492
494   REM
500   DATA  98, 80, 73, 92, 77, 84, 83, 79, 87, 73
510   DATA  99, 63, 63, 92, 81, 93, 47, 53, 89, 100
520   DATA  98, 71, 73, .01
530   END
RUN
MEDIAN

MEDIAN 81
```

As written, MEDIAN does not properly account for an even number of data items.

## Problems for Sec. 11-3

1) Modify program MEDIAN to allow for both even and odd numbers of data items.

2) Modify ØRDER so that it can be used to arrange in either ascending or descending order determined by an INPUT request.

3) Modify MEDIAN as in problem 1 and print the largest, smallest, and average value.

4) Generate 100 random numbers from 1 to 100 and find the median.

5) As written, program ØRDER is efficient for a set of numbers in which only the first number in the list is out of order. But suppose only the last number is out of order. Then the program is slow. We can improve it by inserting an upward sort, taking the number that belongs at the top of the list up to the top in one pass and then not scanning that element again. Incorporate this step into the program.

## 11-4 Coefficient of Linear Correlation

Very often people have a set of data consisting of two or more figures for each object of the study and would like to know if there is a relation between them. For example, suppose we have test scores for five people for whom we also have IQ scores, as shown in Table 11-1. We would like to know if one score is a good predictor of the other score.

TABLE 11-1 IQ's and Test Scores
for Five People

| IQ | TEST |
|-----|------|
| 110 | 80 |
| 105 | 84 |
| 134 | 92 |
| 128 | 71 |
| 92 | 83 |

There is a variety of formula and techniques for finding correlations. We present here a computational formula for finding the degree of linear correlation between two sets of data, $X$ and $Y$.

$$r_{XY} = \frac{n \sum_{i=1}^{n} X_1 Y_1 - \sum_{i=1}^{n} X_1 \sum_{i=1}^{n} Y_1}{n^2 V_X V_Y} \tag{11-1}$$

where $r_{XY}$ is the linear correlation coefficient, $V_X$ is the variance of the $X$ data, and $V_Y$ is the variance of the $Y$ data.

Let's look at the correlation coefficient for the data of Table 11-1. See program CØRREL. The correlation is about .03. That may safely be taken to indicate that there is no correlation between these two sets of data. That is, IQ is unrelated to the test score. We can see by inspection that no obvious pattern is present.

We can get some idea of how the value of $r$ is affected by various patterns in the data by simply using CØRREL with a variety of data. We present two additional runs for your observation.

```
CØRREL
 94   REM * THIS PRØGRAM CALCULATES CØRRELATIØN CØEFFICIENT
100   LET N = S = S1 = S2 = T1 = T2 = 0
110   PRINT "IQ    TEST SCØRE"
120   READ X,Y
130      IF X = 0 THEN 220
140   PRINT X; TAB(6); Y
150   LET N = N+1
152
154   REM * SUMMATIØNS DØNE IN LINES 160 THRØUGH 200
160   LET S = S + X*Y
170   LET S1 = S1+X
180   LET S2 = S2+Y
190   LET T1 = T1 + X↑2
200   LET T2 = T2 + Y↑2
210   GØTØ 120
212
```

```
214   REM * VARIANCES CALCULATED IN LINES 220 THRØUGH 270
220   LET A1 = S1/N
230   LET A2 = S2/N
240   LET B1 = T1/N
250   LET B2 = T2/N
260   LET V1 = SQR( B1 - A1↑2 )
270   LET V2 = SQR( B2 - A2↑2 )
272
280   LET R = ( N*S - S1*S2 )/( (N↑2)*V1*V2 )
290   PRINT
300:  CØRRELATIØN = #.###
310   PRINT USING 300, R
312
314   REM
320   DATA  110,80,   105,84,   134,92
330   DATA  128,71,    92,83,     0, 0
340   END
RUN
CØRREL

IQ    TEST SCØRE
110    80
105    84
134    92
128    71
 92    83

CØRRELATIØN =  .027

RUN
CØRREL

IQ    TEST SCØRE
134    92
128    84
110    83
105    80
 92    71

CØRRELATIØN =  .930

RUN
CØRREL

IQ    TEST SCØRE
 1     -2
 2     -3
 4     -5
 5     -6

CØRRELATIØN = *-1.000
```

We can see that correlation coefficients range from $-1$ to .930 in the sample of runs. It turns out that $-1$ to 1 is the true maximum range. A coefficient of one indicates perfect correlation. A coefficient of zero indicates no correlation, and a coefficient of negative one indicates perfect negative correlation. Generally, values between $-.40$ and .40 are considered to indicate that the variables are unrelated, whereas for $-1$ to $-.9$ and for .9 to 1 the variables are considered to be extremely closely related in a linear fashion. The larger the number of data items we use to calculate the value of $r$, the more reliable its value. For a small amount of data, the coefficient is more likely to be affected by a single stray or inaccurate item of data.

Often it may happen that we have more than two sets of data with which to work. With a slight modification of CØRREL, we can easily find the linear correlation coefficient for columns 1 and 2, 1 and 3, and 2 and 3 for the data shown in Table 11-2. See program runs labelled WEATHER. The program is actually CØRREL with the READ statement modified as shown in each run. An alternative approach would be to RESTØRE the data and use the entire program as a subroutine three times.

TABLE 11-2   Run Table Showing Normal, Record High, and Record Low
Temperatures for 24 Selected Dates of the Year

| Normal | High | Low | Normal | High | Low |
|--------|------|-----|--------|------|-----|
| 32 | 61 | 4 | 32 | 63 | 5 |
| 46 | 81 | 14 | 53 | 91 | 27 |
| 33 | 61 | 2 | 34 | 63 | -2 |
| 58 | 90 | 35 | 63 | 90 | 37 |
| 36 | 68 | 11 | 41 | 86 | 10 |
| 68 | 97 | 44 | 72 | 98 | 44 |
| 74 | 102 | 52 | 76 | 98 | 56 |
| 62 | 89 | 34 | 55 | 89 | 34 |
| 76 | 97 | 56 | 74 | 94 | 56 |
| 50 | 84 | 30 | 44 | 72 | 21 |
| 71 | 97 | 49 | 67 | 93 | 44 |
| 39 | 68 | 11 | 33 | 60 | 7 |

```
120   READ X,Y,Z        120   READ X,Z,Y        120   READ Z,X,Y

RUN                     RUN                     RUN
WEATHER                 WEATHER                 WEATHER

X     Y                 X     Y                 X     Y
32    61                32    4                 61    4
32    63                32    5                 63    5
46    81                46    14                81    14
53    91                53    27                91    27
33    61                33    2                 61    2
34    63                34    -2                63    -2
58    90                58    35                90    35
63    90                63    37                90    37
36    68                36    11                68    11
41    86                41    10                86    10
68    97                68    44                97    44
72    98                72    44                98    44
74    102               74    52                102   52
76    98                76    56                98    56
62    89                62    34                89    34
55    89                55    34                89    34
76    97                76    56                97    56
74    94                74    56                94    56
50    84                50    30                84    30
44    72                44    21                72    21
71    97                71    49                97    49
67    93                67    44                93    44
39    68                39    11                68    11
33    60                33    7                 60    7

CØRRELATIØN = .944     CØRRELATIØN = .984     CØRRELATIØN = .920
```

For correlation normal to high, we get .944; for normal to low, we get .984; and for high to low, we get .920. These all indicate a high degree of linear correlation.

If we were to require the correlation coefficients for all pairs of columns for more than three columns, it is a bit awkward to use the method we used in program WEATHER. It would be a lot cleaner to read all the data into an array and manipulate the column subscripts to get all possible pairs. This is left as an exercise.

## Summary of Sec. 11-4

We have presented a computational formula for obtaining the linear correlation coefficient. This is also referred to as the Pearson $r$. Values close to zero indicate a low degree of linear correlation, whereas values with absolute value close to one indicate a high degree of linear correlation.

## Problems for Sec. 11-4

1) Write a program to generate 25 pairs of random numbers and compute the correlation coefficient. What value do you expect? Run the program several times.

2) Write a program to calculate the correlation coefficient for the integers 2 through 100 and the number of factors.

3) Do problem 2 for prime factors not including 1.

4) Write a program to find correlation coefficients for all pairs of columns by first reading the data into a single array as described in the section. Use the following data:

| a | b | c | d |
|----|----|----|------|
| 39 | 12 | 2 | 1978 |
| 43 | 8 | 5 | 1749 |
| 25 | 4 | 1 | 1462 |
| 22 | 4 | 1 | 1288 |
| 21 | 11 | 11 | 1241 |
| 21 | 7 | 3 | 1176 |
| 32 | 10 | 2 | 1086 |
| 37 | 7 | 12 | 1026 |
| 18 | 2 | 1 | 1003 |
| 30 | 10 | 3 | 971 |

5) For the data given, find any or all of the following linear correlations:

(a) $a$ and $b$
(b) $a^2$ and $b$
(c) $a^3$ and $b$
(d) $a^4$ and $b$
(e) $a$ and $\log (b)$

| a | b |
|----|---------|
| 1 | 1.04631 |
| 2 | 16.5958 |
| 3 | 84.0632 |
| 4 | 266.206 |
| 5 | 651.343 |
| 6 | 1353.51 |
| 7 | 2512.56 |
| 8 | 4294.3 |
| 9 | 6890.5 |
| 10 | 10519 |
| 11 | 15424 |

# 12
# SIMULATION AND GAMES

## 12-1 Introduction

The ability of the computer to store information, generate random numbers, and make decisions makes it well suited for simulations of all kinds. Computers can be programmed to play games. Programs can be written to simulate business activity, social phenomena, and numerous activities in the physical sciences. Computers can be used to conduct gambling enterprises, schedule classes, and manage production schedules. Some situations are dealt with by having the computer investigate all possible alternatives. Other situations are so complex that a procedure must be found that enables the computer to make a best reasonable decision which may not be the best possible decision. For example, it is possible to write an unbeatable tic-tac-toe program. However, the game of chess allows so many possible sequences of moves that it is impossible to write a program for existing computers to investigate them all.

The purpose of this chapter is to present a few examples of simulation and to suggest areas for further investigation.

## 12-2 Lines at the Bank

As the manager of a new bank branch, you are interested in knowing what to expect in the way of teller requirements. You are presented a bank that has five windows. As a preliminary trial, you make the following estimates and assumptions:

1. Assume that there is always a customer waiting with a four-minute transaction when the bank opens at 9 AM.
2. Always open two windows at 9 AM.
3. Customers will tolerate only as many as 10 persons per line; thus when all lines are full, a new window must be opened.

4. During every minute of the day one or two or no customers will enter with equal probability.

5. Every customer after the first has transactions that will last one, two, or three munutes with equal probability.

6. A new customer upon entering the bank goes to the line with the fewest persons. In case of a tie, the customer takes the line closest to the door.

7. The bank closes at 3 PM.

Our job now is to write a computer program that reacts to each of the restrictions above and keeps track of the day's business. One possible simulation is to use two arrays—one from the customer's point of view and one from the window's point of view. Both arrays have five columns, one per window. The customer array has 10 rows to allow as many as 10 people in line. The window array has four rows. The first row contains a '1' to signify that the window is open and a '0' to signify that the window is closed. The second row contains the number of people in line for that window. The third row contains the number of people served since the run began. The fourth row contains the number of minutes that the window has been open. The customer array contains the number of minutes each customer in line will take.

In program LINES, all loops FØR W1 = 1 TØ 5 scan all five windows. Lines 200 and 210 open two loops to keep track of time. H stands for hours and M1 stands for minutes of that hour. Line 240 looks to see if a window is open, and line 250 adds one minute to open time for the window. Line 260 looks to see if anyone is in line at the open window. Lines 390 through 500 search for the line having the fewest people. Numerous other relevant comments appear in the REM statements of program LINES.

```
LINES
94    REM * THIS PRØGRAM SIMULATES LINES AT
95    REM   TELLER WINDØWS ØF A BANK
96
97    REM * ARRAY L IS THE CUSTØMER ARRAY
98    REM   ARRAY R IS THE WINDØW ARRAY
100   DIM L(10,5), R(4,5), A$(4)
105   RANDØMIZE
110   MAT   READ A$
120   MAT R = ZER
130   MAT L = ZER
132
134   REM * ØPEN WINDØWS 1 AND 2 BY PLACING A
135   REM   1 IN RØW 1 ØF CØLUMNS 1 AND 2 IN ARRAY R
140   LET R(1,1) = R(1,2) = 1
142
144   REM * THE FIRST CUSTØMER ENTERS WITH A
145   REM   FØUR MINUTE TRANSACTIØN
150   LET L(1,1) = 4
160   LET R(2,1) = 1
162
164   REM * SET UP LØØPS TØ KEEP TRACK ØF TIME
200   FØR H = 0 TØ 5
210     FØR M1 = 1 TØ 60
220       LET T = 60*H + M1
222
224       REM * THIS LØØP ADJUSTS TIME FØR
225       REM   CUSTØMERS AND WINDØWS
230       FØR W1 = 1 TØ 5
240         IF R(1,W1) = 0 THEN 350
250         LET R(4,W1) = R(4,W1)+1
```

```
260                   IF R(2,W1) = 0 THEN 350
262
264             REM * THERE IS A LINE
265             REM   REDUCE FIRST PERSON'S TIME
270             LET L(1,W1) = L(1,W1)-1
280                   IF L(1,W1) <> 0 THEN 350
282
284             REM * END OF TRANSACTION - MOVE PEOPLE UP IN LINE
290             FOR P= 1 TO R(2,W1)-1
300                   LET L(P,W1) = L(P+1,W1)
310             NEXT P
320             LET L( R(2,W1),W1 ) = 0
322
324             REM * ONE MORE TRANSACTION - ONE LESS PERSON
330             LET R(3,W1) = R(3,W1)+1
340             LET R(2,W1) = R(2,W1)-1
350          NEXT W1
352
354       REM * ENTER 0, 1 OR 2 CUSTOMERS
360       LET C = INT( RND(-1)*3 )
370       FOR C1 = 1 TO C
372
374             REM * SELECT TRANSACTION TIME
380             LET T1 = INT( RND(-1)*3+1 )
382
384             REM * NOW FIND THE SHORTEST LINE WITH
385             REM   LESS THAN TEN PEOPLE
390             LET N = R(2,1)
400             LET N1 = 1
410             FOR W1 = 2 TO 5
420                   IF R(1,W1) = 0 THEN 460
430                   IF R(2,W1) >= N THEN 460
432
434                REM * CURRENT LINE IS SHORTER
435                REM   SAVE WINDOW # AND # OF PEOPLE
440                LET N = R(2,W1)
450                LET N1 = W1
460             NEXT W1
462
500                IF N <= 9 THEN 590
510             FOR W1 = 1 TO 5
520                IF R(1,W1) = 0 THEN 570
530             NEXT W1
532
540             PRINT  "ALL WINDOWS FULL AT"; T; "MINUTES"
550             MAT  PRINT R;
560             STOP
562
564             REM * OPEN ANOTHER WINDOW
570             LET R(1,W1) = 1
580             LET N1 = W1
590             LET R(2,N1) = R(2,N1)+1
600             LET L( R(2,N1),N1 ) = T1
610          NEXT C1
620       NEXT M1
622
630       GOSUB 800
640 NEXT H
650 STOP
652
800 PRINT TAB(11); "AT THE END OF"; T/60; "HOURS"
810 PRINT  "  WINDOW NO.    ONE   TWO   THREE FOUR   FIVE"
820 FOR I = 1 TO 4
830    PRINT A$(I);
840    FOR J = 1 TO 5
850       PRINT TAB(15+(J-1)*6); R(I,J);
860    NEXT J
870    PRINT
880 NEXT I
890 PRINT
900 RETURN
972
```

```
974   REM
980   DATA  "1=OPEN 0=CLOSED",  " PEOPLE IN LINE"
990   DATA  "  PEOPLE SERVED",  " MINUTES OPENED"
999   END
```

RUN
LINES

```
                AT THE END OF 1 HOURS
    WINDOW NO.      ONE    TWO    THREE FOUR  FIVE
1=OPEN 0=CLOSED 1        1      0      0     0
PEOPLE IN LINE 4        4      0      0     0
   PEOPLE SERVED 31      25     0      0     0
MINUTES OPENED 60       60     0      0     0

                AT THE END OF 2 HOURS
    WINDOW NO.      ONE    TWO    THREE FOUR  FIVE
1=OPEN 0=CLOSED 1        1      0      0     0
PEOPLE IN LINE 8        8      0      0     0
   PEOPLE SERVED 59      52     0      0     0
MINUTES OPENED 120     120     0      0     0

                AT THE END OF 3 HOURS
    WINDOW NO.      ONE    TWO    THREE FOUR  FIVE
1=OPEN 0=CLOSED 1        1      0      0     0
PEOPLE IN LINE 9        9      0      0     0
   PEOPLE SERVED 92      79     0      0     0
MINUTES OPENED 180     180     0      0     0

                AT THE END OF 4 HOURS
    WINDOW NO.      ONE    TWO    THREE FOUR  FIVE
1=OPEN 0=CLOSED 1        1      1      0     0
PEOPLE IN LINE 1        0      0      0     0
   PEOPLE SERVED 122    108     23     0     0
MINUTES OPENED 240     240     50     0     0

                AT THE END OF 5 HOURS
    WINDOW NO.      ONE    TWO    THREE FOUR  FIVE
1=OPEN 0=CLOSED 1        1      1      0     0
PEOPLE IN LINE 1        1      1      0     0
   PEOPLE SERVED 148    131     36     0     0
MINUTES OPENED 300     300    110     0     0

                AT THE END OF 6 HOURS
    WINDOW NO.      ONE    TWO    THREE FOUR  FIVE
1=OPEN 0=CLOSED 1        1      1      0     0
PEOPLE IN LINE 1        1      0      0     0
   PEOPLE SERVED 178    153     51     0     0
MINUTES OPENED 360     360    170     0     0
```

The run shows that ten minutes into the fourth hour the third window was opened. We can see that at the end of the day there was one person waiting at window 1, which had served 178 people during the day. Window 2 also had one person in line, but had served only 153 customers. Similarly, the third window had served 51 customers and left none in line at the end of the day's business.

While the results of LINES provide some interesting information, there are virtually unlimited possibilities for extracting more information and for testing changes in the original list of assumptions and estimates.

There have been no provisions for closing a window. We might want to close a window due to lack of activity or to allow employees time to lunch. In practice, bank tellers close windows but service those customers already in line.

Program LINES does not provide for having a window closed with people standing in line. We could use a "-1" in the window array to signify this condition.

It is fairly obvious that the assumption of random arrival of customers is an oversimplification of the true pattern. Clearly, large numbers of people conduct bank business during their lunch hour. Not only does the arrival of customers vary during the day, but it varies with the days of the week and of the month. Fridays tend to be heavier, and the first of the month is heavy.

The limit of 10 persons per line was thus arbitrary and perhaps unreasonable as an absolute limit. The program could be modified to open a new window when all the lines contain 10 customers, but when all windows are open and all lines contain 10, then we should allow the lines to grow.

In practice, a new customer generally steps into the shortest line, but the customer is not obligated to stay there. Thus we could make provision in our simulator for customers to move to a faster moving line. (We know from experience that fast-moving lines immediately become slow-moving lines when we step into them and slow-moving lines immediately become fast-moving lines when we step out of them.) This points up the fact that although a customer enters a line based on the number of customers in it, what he really cares about is how long he has to wait. We could add a row to the window array giving maximum waiting time so far. We could cause a certain waiting time to trigger opening a new window.

As the program is written, when a new window opens only new customers may enter that line. Generally when a new window opens, a whole bunch of people swarm into the new line. Sometimes the new line quickly exceeds the old lines in length. We could modify the simulation of LINES to allow an orderly shift of customers from all lines to a newly opened window.

It is easy to see that we could go on and on at great length, making our simulation program more and more like what we believe to be the real life activity. What about drive-in windows, automatic tellers, etc.?

Based on many runs of simulations like this, a business person is in a better position to make decisions about hiring, opening hours, business procedures, and other aspects of management than he would be without the computer. Once we are convinced that a simulation is realistic, then we can experiment with innovative procedures using computer results to warn us of poor changes without actually having to use customers as guinea pigs.

Similar simulations could be set up for toll booths, grocery store checkouts, post offices, gas stations, and stores and businesses of all kinds.

## Summary of Sec. 12-2

We have looked at a much simplified set of rules for lines at the tellers' windows of a bank and written a program to imitate the activities of bank customers for a sample business day. Random numbers are used to simulate the random nature of the arrival of people at the bank and the random nature of transactions. Arrays have proved very useful for keeping track of many of the activities of our banking model. We recognize that simulations usually must be simplifications of the real activity under study.

## Problems for Sec. 12-2

The possibilities for making changes in program LINES and developing other models are so varied and so numerous that no attempt will be made to enumerate a specific set of problems. Instead you should select one or more of the improvements outlined in this section and implement them, along with any changes not mentioned that you would like to make. You should obtain several runs of your final program to get a range of results. Experiment with differing transaction times, differing rates of arrival of customers, and so forth.

## 12-3 Magic Squares

Magic squares have provided entertainment and been the source of wonder for more than a thousand years. They have been considered to have magic powers and therefore have been used to keep away evil spirits. Magic squares are square arrays of numbers (usually integers) so arranged that all row sums equal all column sums and these equal each of the sums of the elements of the two main diagonals.

Of course, this feat can be accomplished by simply entering the same number in each position of the array, but this is trivial and of little interest. The simplest magic square of real interest is the following three-by-three magic square:

$$8 \quad 1 \quad 6$$
$$3 \quad 5 \quad 7$$
$$4 \quad 9 \quad 2$$

Note that all integers from 1 through 9 have been used and that the magic sum is 15. It turns out that while we can rotate this to get a total of eight different positions, there is no other arrangement of these integers that will produce a magic square, even though there are 45,360 possible different arrangements. The magic sum can be found for integers 1 through $n^2$ by the formula,

$$s = \frac{n^3 + n}{2}$$

An odd order magic square from 3 up can be generated by a procedure called the De la Loubere method. For a 5 × 5 magic square, this method produces only one magic square, but millions are possible. The De la Loubere method uses the integers 1 to $n^2$ for an $n$th-order magic square and may be described with the following set of rules:

1. Begin by entering a "1" in the center column of the first row.
2. Always move diagonally up one and to the right one and enter the next larger integer there unless the move (a) is the move immediately following an entry that is a multiple of the order of the magic square, in which case the new number goes directly beneath the previous one, or, (b) takes us out the side of the square, in which case the new number goes to the extreme left of the new row, or, (c) takes us out the top of the square, in which case the new number goes to the bottom of the new column.
3. Proceeding in this way, $n^2$ should always be placed in the middle column of the bottom row, and we know it is time to stop.

In program MAGIC for $n = 5$, the middle column is determined in line 160, and the row is set to 1 in line 170 so that the first entry in line 190 follows rule 1 above. Line 210 checks to see if the condition in rule 2a has occurred. Line 250 checks for the condition of rule 2b, and line 300 checks on rule 2c. Line 200 determines the stopping point as per rule 3.

```
MAGIC
      94    REM * THIS PRØGRAM GENERATES ØDD ØRDER
      95    REM MAGIC SQUARES BY THE DE LA LØUBERE
      96    REM   METHØD
      100   DIM M(47,47)
      110   PRINT  "WHAT ØDD SIZE";
      120   INPUT N
      130       IF N/2 = INT(N/2) THEN 110
      140   MAT M = ZER(N,N)
      150   LET C1 = 0
  → 160   LET C = INT(N/2)+1
  → 170   LET R = 1
      180   LET C1 = C1+1
  → 190   LET M(R,C) = C1
  → 200       IF C1 = N↑2 THEN 330
  → 210       IF C1/N <> INT(C1/N) THEN 240
      220   LET R = R+1
      230   GØTØ 180
      240   LET C = C+1
  → 250       IF C <= N THEN 290
      260   LET C = 1
      270   LET R = R-1
      280   GØTØ 180
      290   LET R = R-1
  → 300       IF R > 0 THEN 180
      310   LET R = N
      320   GØTØ 180
      330   PRINT
      340   LET T = 0
      342
      344   REM * ADD ØNE CØLUMN TØ FIND MAGIC NUMBER
      350   FØR I = 1 TØ N
      360       LET T = T+M(I,1)
      370   NEXT I
      372
      380   PRINT  "MAGIC NUMBER IS"; T
      390   PRINT
      400   MAT   PRINT M;
      410   END
      RUN
MAGIC

WHAT ØDD SIZE?5

MAGIC NUMBER IS 65

      17    24     1     8     15

      23     5     7    14     16

       4     6    13    20     22

      10    12    19    21      3

      11    18    25     2      9
```

As written, this program will arrange and print magic squares up to 47 by 47. Of course, we can't print 47 numbers across the page. So we would have to do some rearranging to make the results easy to read.

## Problems for Sec. 12-3

1) The magic squares of this section used 1 as the first number. It is easy to show that beginning with any integer will also produce a magic square. Modify program MAGIC to allow beginning with any integer. Be careful about rule 2a.

2) Another way to generate odd order magic squares may be described as follows. Place the first number in the array position directly beneath the central element, and proceed down one row and to the right one column unless this move: (a) takes you both out the bottom and out the right side of the square, in which case the new entry goes in position $(2,n)$, or (b) takes you out the bottom of the square, in which case the new entry goes to the top of the new column, or (c) takes you out the right side of the square, in which case the new entry goes to the extreme left in the new row, or (d) the new location is already occupied, in which case the new entry goes in the second row directly below the previous entry. (Note that this may take you out the bottom.) Write a program to generate this type of odd-order magic square.

3) Squares of the type described in problem 2 can also be generated by beginning with any integer. Modify your program for problem 2 to do this.

4) There are 880 different 4-by-4 magic squares using the integers 1 through 16. One of them can be generated by the following simple procedures: MAT READ the integers 1 through 16 into a 4-by-4 array and then make these exchanges:

$$A(1,1) \rightleftharpoons A(4,4)$$
$$A(2,2) \rightleftharpoons A(3,3)$$
$$A(3,2) \rightleftharpoons A(2,3)$$
$$A(4,1) \rightleftharpoons A(1,4)$$

Write a program to do this.

## 12-4  Games

There are hundreds of games which may be played with computers. There are games played with cards, dice, dominoes, and numbers. There are board games and two- and three-dimensional tic-tac-toe. Programs have been written to play casino gambling games and to simulate slot machines. There are programs which simulate horse races. Programs can be written to play word games such as Hangman or Geography using strings and files. Using computer files, game-playing programs can be devised which modify strategy depending on consequences of previous decisions. It is not the purpose of this section to present any comprehensive or systematic study of games or game strategy. Rather, it is the purpose of this section to arouse the sleeping giant of gamesmanship that may lie within the reader by exploring two examples.

## Battle of Numbers

The game, Battle of Numbers, begins with two integers, such as 63 and 11, where one should always be somewhat larger than the other. Two players take turns subtracting an integer in the range 1 to 11 from 63 and subsequent new remainders. The last player to subtract loses. The feature that makes this game intriguing is that usually the first player may assure a win by applying proper strategy on the very first move. Working out the strategy is fairly straightforward if we look at the last few moves. Suppose it is your turn, and you may subtract up to 11 from 15. If you subtract 2 leaving 13, you win because your opponent must leave you a number in the range of 2 to 12, subtracting in the range 11 to 1. Now it is your turn again and you can be assured of leaving your opponent a "1," which he must subtract, thereby losing. Now one pair of plays earlier you can assure yourself of leaving your opponent with 13 by leaving 25 and before that 37, and so forth. That is, you want to leave $(11 + 1) i + 1$, or one more than an integral multiple of one more than the largest number you are allowed to subtract. For subtracting in the range 1 to $a$, then leave $(a + 1) i + 1$. This means that if the human player goes first in competition with the computer, the human can always win except when the original larger number is one more than an integral multiple of the largest subtractable number. However, one slip-up, and the computer can always win.

Thus in our game with 63 as the starting total and 11 as the maximum subtractable integer, divide 63 by 12 to get 5 as the integral quotient. Since 5 times 12 is 60, if we are faced with 61 we can't win and should subtract some random integer. But since we are not faced with 61, we want to leave our opponent with 61 by subtracting 2. No matter what our opponent does, we will leave 49, then 37, then 13, then 1. The calculations and testing here are done in lines 370 through 410 of program BATTLE. Note that lines 280 through 320 assure that the human player inputs a number in the range 1 to $a$. If you would like to play the game, but don't want to type the program, many timesharing systems include the game under the name BATNUM.

```
BATTLE

94     REM * THIS PROGRAM PLAYS BATTLE OF NUMBERS
100    PRINT TAB(15); "BATTLE OF NUMBERS"
105    RANDOMIZE
110    PRINT "DO YOU KNOW THE RULES";
120    INPUT A$
130       IF A$ = "YES" THEN 180
140    PRINT  "WE TAKE TURNS SUBTRACTING AN INTEGER IN THE"
150    PRINT  "INTERVAL 1 TO SOME NUMBER A FROM ANOTHER NUMBER"
160    PRINT  "B WITH THE DIFFERENCE LEAVING B FOR THE NEXT"
170    PRINT  "TURN. THE LAST PERSON TO TAKE LOSES."
180    PRINT  "HERE WE GO. ***"
182
184    REM * SELECT RANGE AND STARTING NUMBER
185    REM   THE RESTRICTING CONSTANTS HERE ARE ARBITRARY
190    LET A = INT( RND(-1)*14+7 )
200    LET B = INT( RND(-1)*77+41 )
210    PRINT
220    PRINT  "INTERVAL = 1 TO"; A
230    PRINT
240    PRINT  "STARTING TOTAL IS"; B
250    PRINT
```

```
260   PRINT  "YØU GØ";
270   INPUT P
272
274     REM * CHECK FØR AN INTEGER IN THE LEGAL RANGE
275     REM  LESS THAN ØR EQUAL TØ THE REMAINING TØTAL
280     IF P <> INT(P) THEN 310
290     IF INT((P-1)/A) <> 0 THEN 310
300     IF P <= B THEN 330
310   PRINT  "ILLEGAL MØVE"
320   GØTØ 250
330   LET B = B-P
340     IF B > 0 THEN 370
350   PRINT  "*** I WIN ***"
360   STOP
370   LET I = INT( (B-1)/(A+1) )
380   LET C = B - ( (A+1)*I+1 )
390     IF C > 0 THEN 420
400   LET C = INT( RND(-1)*A+1 )
410     IF B-C < 0 THEN 400
420   LET B = B-C
430   PRINT  "I TAKE"; C
440     IF B = 0 THEN 470
450   PRINT  "LEAVING A TØTAL ØF"; B
460   GØTØ 250
470   PRINT  "*** YØU WIN ***"
480   END


RUN
BATTLE

                    BATTLE ØF NUMBERS
DØ YØU KNØW THE RULES? YES
HERE WE GØ. ***

INTERVAL = 1 TØ 20

STARTING TØTAL IS 68

YØU GØ? 4
I TAKE 6
LEAVING A TØTAL ØF 58

YØU GØ? 15
I TAKE 7
LEAVING A TØTAL ØF 36

YØU GØ? 14
I TAKE 6
LEAVING A TØTAL ØF 16

YØU GØ? 15
I TAKE 1
*** YØU WIN ***
```

## The Knight's Tour

The game of chess is played on a square board having 64 smaller squares, eight on a side. The various pieces belonging to the two sides are assigned specific moves. The knight moves in an L-shaped path, moving one square in any direction and two squares in a direction perpendicular to the first move. Thus from a position near the center of the chess board, a knight may move to any of eight possible positions. If the knight occupies position (3, 4), then he may move to any one of the following: (4, 6), (4, 2), (2, 6), (2, 2), (5, 5), (5, 3), (1, 5) or (1, 3). In general, if the knight occupies position $(r, c)$, then he may move to any of the following: $(r + 1, c + 2)$, $(r + 1, c - 2)$, $(r - 1, c + 2)$, $(r - 1, c - 2)$, $(r + 2, c + 1)$, $(r + 2, c - 1)$, $(r - 2, c + 1)$, or $(r - 2, c - 1)$, unless the new position is off the board. An ancient and intriguing challenge is to move the knight about the board in such a way that it visits all 64 squares of the chess board exactly once.

This is a difficult feat, known as the Knight's Tour, but it can be done. We will here contrive only to select moves randomly until the knight reaches a dead end due to the fact that all reachable squares have already been visited. We use an 8-by-8 array B to simulate the board. Initially all entries are zero to indicate open positions. We will place the move numbers in the squares as the knight moves about the board. The 8-by-2 array U stores all eight possible moves from the present position as described in the previous paragraph. These eight moves are scanned for legal use in lines 220, 230, and 240 of program TØUR. Note that INT $((R1 - 1)/8) = 0$ in line 220 is equivalent to $(0 < R1$

```
TØUR

94    REM * THIS PRØGRAM CARRIES ØUT A RANDØM
95    REM  KNIGHT'S TØUR TØ DEAD END
100   DIM B(8,8),T(2,8),U(8,2)
110   MAT B = ZER
120   MAT READ U
130   LET M = 1
140   PRINT  "BEGIN WHERE";
150   INPUT R, C
160   LET B(R,C) = M
170   MAT T = ZER
172
174   REM * K1 CØUNTS THE NUMBER ØF LEGAL MØVES
180   LET K1 = 0
182
184   REM * ENTER ALL LEGAL MØVES IN T ARRAY
190   FØR T = 1 TØ 8
200      LET R1 = R + U(T,1)
210      LET C1 = C + U(T,2)
220         IF INT( (R1-1)/8 ) <> 0 THEN 280
230         IF INT( (C1-1)/8 ) <> 0 THEN 280
240         IF B(R1,C1) <> 0 THEN 280
250      LET K1 = K1+1
260      LET T(1,K1) = R1
270      LET T(2,K1) = C1
280   NEXT T
282
290      IF K1 = 0 THEN 350
292
294   REM * SELECT A LEGAL MØVE AT RANDØM
300   LET T = INT( RND(-1)*K1+1 )
310   LET R = T(1,T)
320   LET C = T(2,T)
330   LET M = M+1
340   GØTØ 160
342
350   PRINT  "GØT TØ"; M
360   PRINT  "PRINT IT";
370   INPUT A$
380      IF A$ <> "YES" THEN 420
390   MAT PRINT B;
392
394   REM
400   DATA 1,2, 1,-2, -1,2, -1,-2
410   DATA 2,1, 2,-1, -2,1, -2,-1
420   END
RUN
TØUR
```

```
BEGIN WHERE?4,4
GØT TØ 41
PRINT IT?YES
```

| 0 | 8 | 15 | 0 | 0 | 24 | 39 | 0 |
|---|---|----|---|---|----|----|---|
| 14 | 11 | 0 | 7 | 38 | 0 | 0 | 25 |
| 0 | 16 | 9 | 12 | 0 | 26 | 23 | 40 |
| 10 | 13 | 18 | 1 | 6 | 37 | 0 | 0 |
| 17 | 0 | 5 | 36 | 27 | 22 | 41 | 0 |
| 0 | 0 | 2 | 19 | 32 | 35 | 28 | 0 |
| 0 | 0 | 0 | 4 | 0 | 30 | 21 | 34 |
| 0 | 3 | 0 | 31 | 20 | 33 | 0 | 29 |

AND R1<9). If a move is found to be legal, then we enter it into the T array. When all legal moves are in the Array T, K1 is the number of legal moves. If K1 is zero, then the knight has reached a dead end and we may print the tour or not. We present a flowchart in two parts. Figure 12-1 details the sorting out of legal next moves. Figure 12-2 shows where a legal move chosen at random is incorporated into the tour.

### Summary of Sec. 12-4

We have seen programs to play Battle of Numbers and simulate the Knight's Tour. In the first case there is a guaranteed strategy which we exploit in our program. In the second case we have not employed strategy of any kind but merely progress from step to legal step at random with no procedure for maximizing results.

### Projects for Sec. 12-4

Some of the projects listed will require considerable study and planning before the actual coding of the program takes place. Be sure to allow a reasonable amount of time should you attempt any of the longer projects. Some of the solution programs can be very long indeed. The reader needn't feel limited to projects proposed here.

1) Modify the game of Battle of Numbers so that the last person to take away wins. Be sure to change the computer's strategy.
2) Write a program to play the game of Nim.
3) Write a program to play Tic-Tac-Toe. First decide whether or not you want an unbeatable program.
4) Write a program to play three-dimensional Tic-Tac-Toe.
5) Write a program to lengthen the knight's tour by backing up every time the knight hits a dead end.
6) Write a program to play the game of Geography using strings and files. In this game two players take turns naming places where the first letter of the new place must be the last letter of the last place named.
7) Write a program to make the computer the dealer in a blackjack game.
8) Write a program to play craps.
9) Write a program to simulate a Roulette-wheel.

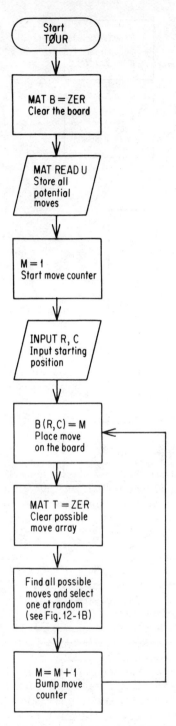

**Figure 12-1**  Flowchart for keeping track of Knight's Tour.

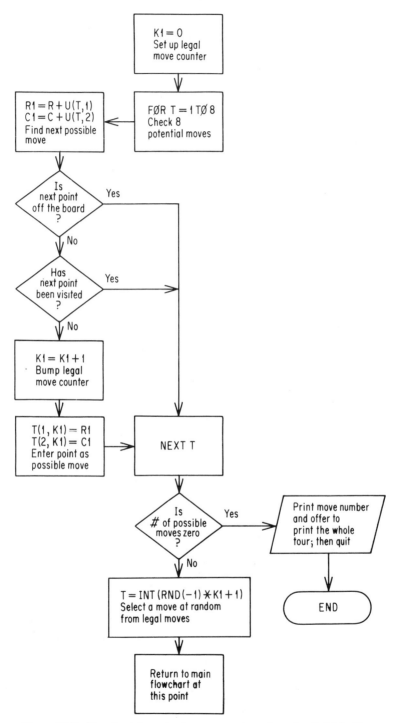

**Figure 12-2** Flowchart for selecting moves at random for Knight's Tour.

# APPENDIX A

## ASCII Character Set Printable on Model 33

| CØDE | CHARACTER | CØDE | CHARACTER |
|------|-----------|------|-----------|
| 32 |   | 64 | @ |
| 33 | ! | 65 | A |
| 34 | " | 66 | B |
| 35 | # | 67 | C |
| 36 | $ | 68 | D |
| 37 | % | 69 | E |
| 38 | & | 70 | F |
| 39 | ' | 71 | G |
| 40 | ( | 72 | H |
| 41 | ) | 73 | I |
| 42 | * | 74 | J |
| 43 | + | 75 | K |
| 44 | , | 76 | L |
| 45 | - | 77 | M |
| 46 | . | 78 | N |
| 47 | / | 79 | Ø |
| 48 | 0 | 80 | P |
| 49 | 1 | 81 | Q |
| 50 | 2 | 82 | R |
| 51 | 3 | 83 | S |
| 52 | 4 | 84 | T |
| 53 | 5 | 85 | U |
| 54 | 6 | 86 | V |
| 55 | 7 | 87 | W |
| 56 | 8 | 88 | X |
| 57 | 9 | 89 | Y |
| 58 | : | 90 | Z |
| 59 | ; | 91 | [ |
| 60 | < | 92 | \ |
| 61 | = | 93 | ] |
| 62 | > | 94 | ↑ |
| 63 | ? | 95 | ← |

NØTE SPECIAL CHARACTERS:

```
LINEFEED ØR CTRL J      10
FØRMFEED ØR CTRL L      12
RETURN ØR CTRL M        13
SPACE                   32
```

# APPENDIX B

## Summary of Flowchart Shapes

Terminal

Used for beginning and ending of program.

Indicates data entered into the computer or results returned by the computer.

| READ | MAT READ | READ# |
|------|----------|-------|
| PRINT | MAT PRINT | READ: |
| INPUT | MAT INPUT | WRITE# |
| | | WRITE: |

Decision

Indicates that a decision is being made.

IF    XXXXXX    THEN    YYY

Indicates a sequence of program statements not included in the flowchart. May be used for GØSUB statement.

Connector. Indicates transfer from one statement to another other than the next higher numbered statement in the program. N matches another N elsewhere in the same flowchart.

Operation
Opens loop
Closes loop

Used for anything not already specified.

NEXT X
LET
RETURN
STØP

# APPENDIX C

## Summary of Statements in BASIC

*NOTE: Not all statements which appear in this appendix will run on all systems and the list here does not cover every statement for some systems.*

| | |
|---|---|
| END | It is the highest numbered statement of every BASIC program. It is optional on a few systems and required on most. |
| PRINT | Prints values of variables, calculated values, and literal expressions inside quotes. Spacing is controlled by commas, semicolons, and TAB. More spacing functions are available on some systems. |
| PRINT USING n | Prints according to format specified in line n. |
| : | Specifies printing for PRINT USING statements. |
| READ | Enters values stored in DATA statements into variables named in the READ statement. All legal BASIC variables (string and numeric) may be read in a single READ statement by separating them with commas. |
| DATA | Stores values for READ statements. Items of data must be separated by commas. Some systems require that strings be in quotes. |
| GØTØ n | Names $n$ as the next line number to be executed by the computer. |
| ØN X GØTØ $n_1, n_2, n_3$, etc., or GØTØ X ØF $n_1, n_2, n_3$, etc., or GØTØ $n_1, n_2, n_3$, etc., ØN X | Computed GØTØ goes to the line number in the $x$th position in the list of line numbers $n_1, n_2, n_3$, etc. If available, one of these should work. They are not interchangeable. |
| LET | Assignment statement. The word LET is optional on many systems. Stores the value on the right of an equals sign in the variable named on the left. May be used to assign string variables. Multiple assignment is available on most systems. |
| REM | Permits the programmer to remark upon the program in the program itself without affecting the pro- |

|                          |                                                                                                                                                                  |
|--------------------------|------------------------------------------------------------------------------------------------------------------------------------------------------------------|
|                          | gram operation. Some systems allow ' to serve the same purpose.                                                                                                   |
| IF THEN n                | Tests the truth of an algebraic sentence placed between the IF and the THEN. Sends the computer to line n if the sentence is true. Control passes to the next line if the sentence is false. |
| FØR X = A TØ B STEP C    | Opens a machine loop with first value for X at A, last number B, and increment C. If C is omitted, the step defaults to an increment of 1.                         |
| NEXT X                   | Closes machine loop. Sends the computer to the corresponding FØR statement to increment and test X.                                                               |
| GØSUB n                  | Sends the computer to a subroutine beginning at line n. Upon executing a RETURN statement, the computer returns to the line immediately following GØSUB n.         |
| ØN X GØSUB $n_1, n_2, n_3$, etc., or GØSUB X ØF $n_1, n_2, n_3$, etc., or GØSUB X ØN $n_1, n_2, n_3$, etc. | Computed GØSUB goes to the subroutine beginning at the $x$th line number in the list. Upon executing a RETURN statement, control goes to the line immediately following this statement. If available, one of these should work. They are not interchangeable. |
| RETURN                   | Closes all subroutines.                                                                                                                                           |
| DEF FNA(X) =             | Program-defined function. The letter pair FN designates that a function is called for. The function name is A, and the argument is X. Any letter of the alphabet may be used. Some systems permit multiple arguments separated by commas. |
| DEF FNA(X)               | Opening line of a multiple-line program-defined function. Several arguments may be permitted, separated by commas. A value must be assigned to FNA in the lines to follow. |
| FNEND                    | Closing statement of a multiple-line, program-defined function.                                                                                                   |
| STØP                     | Execution of the STØP statement causes termination of the RUN at that point.                                                                                      |
| DIM A( ),B$( ). . . .    | Declares dimensions for one- or two-dimensional numeric arrays or string arrays or both. One number is required in the parentheses for a list and two numbers separated by a comma are required for a two-dimensional array. |
| INPUT                    | Same as READ except that data is to be typed on the keyboard of the remote terminal.                                                                              |
| RESTØRE                  | Restores all data in the program. The next item of data to be read will be the very first data item in the program.                                               |
| RESTØRE*                 | Restores numeric data only.                                                                                                                                       |
| RESTØRE$                 | Restores string data only.                                                                                                                                        |

| | |
|---|---|
| RESTØRE n | Restores all data from line n on. |
| CHANGE A$ TØ A | Stores the ASCII code of the characters of the string A$ in the array A with the length of the string in characters stored in A(0). |
| CHANGE A TØ A$ | Stores a string in A$ with length specified in A(0) and characters determined by the ASCII code stored in the array elements of the A list. |
| RANDØMIZE | Causes the random numbers generated in successive runs of the same program to vary. |

## MATRIX INSTRUCTIONS

| | |
|---|---|
| MAT READ | Enters data into numeric and string arrays. Several arrays can be read in the same MAT READ statement by separating the array names with commas. |
| MAT PRINT | Prints the array(s) listed, separated by commas or semicolons. The delimiter used specifies spacing for the preceding array. Numeric and string arrays are allowed. |
| MAT INPUT | Enters data into an array (string or numeric) from the keyboard. Some systems allow more than one array listed here; others do not. |
| MAT C = A * B | Enters the product of A and B into array C. |
| MAT A = B + C | Enters the sum of B and C into array A. |
| MAT A = B - C | Enters the difference of B and C into array A. |
| MAT A = (K)*B | Multiplies each entry of B by the scalar K and enters the result into A. |
| MAT A = ZER | Creates the zero matrix (fills each entry of A with zero). ZER may be followed by redimensioning specifications in parentheses. |
| MAT A = CØN | Fills each element of A with 1. CØN may be followed by redimensioning specifications in parentheses. |
| MAT E = IDN | Forms the identity matrix E. E must be square. All elements with equal row and column numbers are 1 and all other elements are 0. IDN may be followed by redimensioning specifications in parentheses. |
| MAT X = INV(A) | Finds the inverse of A and enters it in X (if it exists). |
| MAT A = TRN(B) | Fills A with the transpose of B. |

## FUNCTIONS

| | |
|---|---|
| SQR(X) | Computes the non-negative square root of X. X must be non-negative. |
| ABS(X) | Computes the absolute value of X. |
| SGN(X) | Returns the value 1 for X positive, 0 for X equals zero, and -1 for X negative. |

| | |
|---|---|
| INT(X) | Returns integer part of X. For some systems this is the mathematically greatest integer function. For others, the computer simply chops off the digits to the right of the decimal point. (The results are the same for non-negative numbers.) |
| RND(X) | Generates a random number. In some systems the set of random numbers accessed is determined by the value of X. Some systems generate the same set of numbers each time the program is run, whereas others provide a different set and still others provide an option. See RND below. |
| SIN(X),CØS(X),TAN(X) | Computes the sin, cos, or tan of X, where X must be in radians. |
| ATN(X) | Computes the arctan of X. ATN(X) is in radians. The program must be written to determine the correct quadrant for the result. |
| LØG(X) | Computes the logarithm of X using base e. |
| EXP(X) | Computes the number whose LØG base e is X. |
| TAB(X) | Moves the printing mechanism to the (X + 1)st position of the carriage unless the printing mechanism is already past that point, in which case there is no effect. |
| ASC( ) | Returns the ASCII code for the character placed in parentheses. |
| LEN(A$) | Returns the number of characters in the string A$. |
| EXT$(A$,I,J) | String extract function. Isolates a substring in A$ from the Ith to the Jth character inclusive. |
| NUM | Returns the number of elements typed in response to the most recent MAT INPUT statement executed in the program. |
| DET | Returns the determinant of the most recent matrix for which the inverse has been found with the MAT INV ( ) statement. No argument required. |
| RND | Returns a random number. The numbers will be the same on successive runs of the program if the RANDØMIZE statement is not present in the program and different on successive runs if the RANDØMIZE statement is present. |

## FILES

Hewlett Packard Files

| | |
|---|---|
| FILES | Names files to be used by the present program and makes them available for access. File names are separated by commas. |
| READ #N,R | Sets the file pointer to the beginning of the Rth record of the Nth file named in the files statement. In addition, when followed by a semicolon and |

|  |  |
|---|---|
|  | variable list, this statement reads values from the file to the variables. |
| READ #N; | When followed by a variable list, this statement reads from the file at a point previously established. |
| MAT READ # | Reads values from a file with the same options allowed for READ #. |
| PRINT #N,R | Sets the file pointer in the Nth file named in the files statement to the beginning of the Rth record and erases the contents of that record. In addition, when followed by a semicolon and a variable list, this statement causes the contents of the variables to be printed into the file. |
| PRINT #N; | When followed by a variable list this statement causes the contents of the variables to be printed wherever the file pointer has been previously set. |
| MAT PRINT # | Prints values from a matrix to a file with the same options as for PRINT #. |
| IF END #N THEN n | When executed, this statement sets a flag. If at any later time an attempt is made to read past the end of data or past the physical end of the file or to print past the physical end of the file, control passes to line n. |
| TYP(N) | The TYP (N) function takes on values from 1 to 4, depending on the nature of the next information in the file. TYP(N) becomes 1 for number, 2 for string, and 3 for end of file. If the argument is negative, the value 4 will be returned for end of record. |

General Electric Files

|  |  |
|---|---|
| FILES | Names files to be used by the current program and makes them available for access. File names are separated by semicolons. |

ASCII Files

|  |  |
|---|---|
| READ #N, | Reads data from the Nth file named in the program into the variables of the variable list following the comma. |
| WRITE #N, | Writes data from the variable list following the comma to the file. The variables in the list may be separated by semicolons or commas to achieve corresponding spacing in the file. |
| IF MØRE #N | Determines whether or not there is more data in the file. |
| IF END #N | Determines whether or not the end of the file has been reached. |
| APPEND #N | Allows additional data to be written to an existing |

file by setting the file pointer to the end of the
Nth file and placing the file in write mode.

SCRATCH #N          Sets the pointer of the Nth file to the beginning of
the file, erases the file, and places it in write mode.

RESTORE #N          Sets the pointer of the Nth file to the beginning of
the file and places it in the read mode.

## Binary Sequential Files

Binary sequential files may be processed by all of the above statements by substituting a colon (:) for the pound sign (#). Binary files should be less expensive to work with; however, ASCII files are very convenient due to the fact that they may be listed at the terminal.

## Random Access Files

READ :N,            Same as ASCII.

WRITE :N,           Same as ASCII.

IF MØRE :N          Tests true, except when the file pointer is at the
physical end of file.

IF END :N           Tests false, except when the file pointer is at the
physical end of file.

SCRATCH :N          Places the file pointer at the beginning of the file and
fills the file with binary zeros.

RESTØRE :N          Places the file pointer at the beginning of the file
without altering the contents of the file.

SETW N TØ X         Places the file pointer to the Xth word of file N. To
access a random file by record, the formula
$W*(R - 1) + 1$ places the pointer at the beginning of the Rth record if there are W words per record.

# APPENDIX D

## Index of Programs in Text

# BIBLIOGRAPHY

Albrecht, Robert L., LeRoy Finkel and Jerold R. Brown, *BASIC*, Wiley, 1973. Programmed instruction is used to introduce BASIC.

Coan, James S., *Basic BASIC*, Hayden, 1970. An introduction to BASIC in a mathematics setting.

Gateley, Wilson Y., and Gary G. Bitter, *BASIC for Beginners*, McGraw-Hill Book Company, 1970. Brief introduction to the rudiments of BASIC.

Gruenberger, Fred, and George Jaffray, *Problems for Computer Solution*, Wiley, 1965. A book of problems from a wide variety of topics.

Kemeny, John G., and Thomas E. Kurtz, *BASIC Programming*, 2nd Ed., Wiley, 1971. BASIC programming presented by the originators of the language.

Knuth, Donald E., *The Art of Computer Programming*, Vol. 3, *Sorting and Searching*, Addison-Wesley, 1973. A comprehensive treatment on arranging data in order and locating items in an ordered data structure.

Ledgard, Henry F., *Programming Proverbs*, Hayden, 1975. Writing programs that work the first time.

Nolan, Richard L., *Introduction to Computing Through the BASIC Language*, Holt, Rinehart and Winston, 1969. Introduction to computers and computing as well as BASIC.

Pavlovich, Joseph P. and Thomas E. Tahan, *Computer Programming in BASIC*, Holden-Day, 1971. An introduction to BASIC assuming a traditional background in high-school mathematics.

Pegels, C. Carl, *BASIC A computer Programming Language*, Holden-Day, 1973. With business and management applications.

Sage, Edwin R., *Problem Solving with the Computer*, Entlek, 1969. An introduction to BASIC using mathematics problems.

Smith, Robert E., *Discovering BASIC*, Hayden, 1970. Introduces BASIC using a wide variety of interesting problems.

Spencer, Donald D., *A Guide to BASIC Programming; A Time-Sharing Language*, Addison-Wesley, 1970. Introduces the language, solves problems from general interest topics, and presents problems for reader solution.

Spencer, Donald D., *Game Playing with Computers*, Rev. 2nd Ed., Hayden, 1975. Mostly Fortran with some BASIC. Detailed anaylsis of a wide variety of games.

# ANSWERS TO SELECTED PROBLEMS

Each two-page spread should be read from top to bottom as an individual page.

## Chapter 1

### Section 1-2

#### Number 2

```
94   REM * FIND LARGEST AND SMALLEST NUMBER FROM DATA
95
96   REM * READ FIRST NUMBER
100  READ N
102
104  REM * FIRST VALUE IS LARGEST AND SMALLEST SO FAR
110  LET S = L = N
120
130  READ N
140  IF N = -.01 THEN 200
142  IF S <= N THEN 170
144  REM * CURRENT NUMBER SMALLER SO SAVE
150  LET S = N
170  GOTO 120
172  IF L >= N THEN 120
174  REM * CURRENT NUMBER LARGER SO SAVE
180  LET L = N
190  GOTO 120
200  PRINT " LARGEST ="; L
210  PRINT "SMALLEST ="; S
212
214  REM
220  DATA  83, 54, 71, 92, -3, -.01
230  END
RUN
NO.2

LARGEST = 92
SMALLEST =-3
```

#### Number 4

```
94   REM * SUM INTEGERS FROM 1 TO N
100  PRINT "SUM 1 TO";
110  INPUT N
120  LET T = I = 0
130  LET I = I+1
140  LET T = T+I
150  IF I < N THEN 130
160  PRINT T
```

#### Number 2

```
94   REM * FIND GREATEST INTEGER WITHOUT INT FUNCTION
100  READ X
110  IF X = -.00' THEN 290
120  PRINT "INT("; XJ ") IS ";
130  IF X <= 0 THEN 160
140  PRINT X
150  GOTO 100
152
170  IF X > 0 THEN 230
180  LET C = C-1
190  LET X = X+1
200  IF X < 0 THEN 180
210  PRINT C
220  GOTO 100
222
230  LET C = C+1
240  LET X = X-1
250  IF X >= 1 THEN 230
270  PRINT C
272  GOTO 100
274  REM
280  DATA  2, 1.23456, -2.8712, 1, 0, -4, -.001
290  END
NO.2

INT( 2       ) IS  2
INT( 1.23456 ) IS  1
INT(-2.8712  ) IS -3
INT( 1       ) IS  1
INT( 0       ) IS  0
INT(-4       ) IS -4
```

#### Number 4

```
94   REM * TO DEAL FOUR 13 CARD HANDS
100  DIM D(52)
110  PRINT " HANDS"
120  PRINT "ONE", "TWO", "THREE", "FOUR"
130  FOR I = 1 TO 52
140  LET D(I) = I
152  NEXT I
160  LET N = 52
170  FOR R = 1 TO 13
180  FOR H = 1 TO 4
```

```
230  DATA  1001, 1300,  0, 0
232
234  REM * THE EUCLIDEAN ALGORITHM
235  REM   WOULD BE MORE EFFICIENT
240  END
RUN
NO.8

FIRST        SECOND #     G.C.F.
50           35           5
28           39           1
1001         1300         13
```

### Number 10

```
94   REM * COUNT FREQUENCY OF OCCURANCE FOR RANDOM INTEGERS
100  DIM S(10)
102
104  REM * INITIALIZE COUNTING LIST
110  FOR I = 1 TO 10
120  LET S(I) = 0
130  NEXT I
132
134  REM * GENERATE 100 RANDOM INTEGERS COUNT IN LINE 160
140  FOR I = 1 TO 100
150  LET N = INT( RND(-I)*10+1 )
160  LET S(N) = S(N) + 1
170  NEXT I
172
174  REM * PRINT RESULTS
180  FOR I = 1 TO 10
190  PRINT I; S(I)
200  NEXT I
202
210  END
RUN
NO.10

1    14
2    14
3    7
4    10
5    12
6    10
7    8
8    14
9    8
10   14
```

Section 1-4

Number 2

```
94   REM * FINDS MAX AND MIN FOR DEFINED FUNCTION
100  DEF FNR(X) = 13*X†3 - 2*SIN(X†2) - LOG(ABS(15*X))
110  INPUT F,L,I
120  PRINT F,L,I
130  LET M = M1 = FNR(F)
140  LET P = P1 = F
150  FOR X = F+I TO L STEP I
160    IF M <= FNR(X) THEN 200
170      LET M = M1 = FNR(X)
180      LET P = X
190      GOTO 230
200    IF M1 >= FNR(X) THEN 230
210      LET M1 = FNR(X)
220      LET X = X
230  NEXT X
232
240  PRINT M; "MINIMUM AT"; P
250  PRINT M1; "MAXIMUM AT"; P1
260  END
     RUN
NO.2

F,L,I?1,22,.5
8.60901       MINIMUM AT 1
138418.       MAXIMUM AT 22
```

Number 3

```
94   REM * KEEPS SCORE IN A GAME OF TIC TAC TOE
100  DIM X(3,3), P(2), W(4)
110  PRINT "THE BOARD"
120  FOR I = 1 TO 3
130    READ A(I,J)
140  NEXT I
150  NEXT I
160
172
180  LET P1 = 0
180  GOSUB 400
190  FOR Z = 1 TO 2
200    LET P1 = P1 + 1
210    IF P1 = 10 THEN 250
220      PRINT "IT'S A DRAW"
230      GOSUB 400
240    STOP
250    GOSUB 500
260    GOSUB 600
270  NEXT Z
280  GOTO 180
392
394  REM * PRINT THE BOARD
400  FOR I = 1 TO 3
410    FOR J = 1 TO 3
420      PRINT A(I,J);
430    NEXT J
440    PRINT
450  NEXT I
452  RETURN
460  PRINT "ILLEGAL MOVE"
492
494  REM * INPUT MOVES AND CHECK FOR 1 TO 9
500  PRINT "#"; Z;
510  INPUT P(Z)
520  IF (P(Z)-1)/9 <> 0 THEN 490
530  LET P = Z
540  RETURN
592
594  REM * ENTER NEW MOVE AND CHECK FOR WIN
600  LET I = 0
610  FOR I = 1 TO 3
620    LET C = C + 1
630    FOR J = 1 TO 3
640      IF C < P(Z) THEN 710
650      IF A(I,J) = P(Z) THEN 690
```

---

```
170  END
     RUN
NO.4

SUM 1 TO?5
    15
```

Number 5

```
94   REM * FIND FACTORIAL N
100  PRINT "FACTORIAL";
110  INPUT N
120  LET F = 1
130  LET I = 0
140  LET I = I + 1
150  LET F = F*I
160  IF I < N THEN 140
170  PRINT F
180  END
     RUN
NO.5

FACTORIAL?5
    120
```

Number 6

```
94   REM * TO SOLVE EQUATIONS OF THE FORM
95   REM   AX+B = CX+D
100  READ A, B, C, D
110  IF A <> 0 THEN 140
120  IF B <> 0 THEN 140
130  STOP
140  PRINT A; "X+("; B; ") = ("; C; ")X+("; D; ") ";
150  IF A-C <> 0 THEN 180
160  PRINT "NO SOLUTION"
170  GOTO 100
180  PRINT "  SOLUTION X = "; (D-B)/(A-C)
190  GOTO 100
194  REM
200  DATA 1,3,2,-1,   3,2,1,-3
210  DATA 2,-1,2,-3,  0,0,0,0
220  END
     RUN
NO.6
```

```
1 X+( 3 ) = ( 2 )X+(-1 )    SOLUTION X =  4.
3 X+( 2 ) = ( 1 )X+(-3 )    SOLUTION X = -2.5
2 X+(-1 ) = ( 2 )X+(-3 )    NO SOLUTION
```

Chapter 1

Section 1-3

Number 1

```
94   REM * FIND ABS(X) WITHOUT COMPUTER FUNCTIONS
100  IF X = -.001 THEN 190
110  PRINT "ABS("; X; ") = ";
120  IF X > 0 THEN 160
140  PRINT X
150  GOTO 100
160  PRINT -X
170  GOTO 100
172  REM
174  DATA -5, 0, 3, -2, 2.4, -.001
190  END
     RUN
NO.1

ABS(-5 ) =    5
ABS( 0 ) =    0
ABS( 3 ) =    3
ABS(-2 ) =    2
ABS( 2.4 ) =  2.4
```

---

```
182
184  REM * SELECT A CARD AT RANDOM
190  LET C = INT( RND(-1)*N+1 )
200  LET C1 = D(C)
202
204  REM * FIND SUIT
210  LET S = INT( (C1-1)/13 +1 )
212
214  REM * FIND CARD IN SUIT
220  LET C2 = C1 - 13*13
230  IF C2 > 10 THEN 270
240    IF C2 = 1 THEN 560
250    PRINT C2;
260    GOTO 280
270  GOTO C2-10 OF 500,520,540
280  GOTO S OF 600,620,640,660
300  LET D(C) = D(N)
310  LET N = N-1
320    PRINT
330  NEXT R
340  END
342
500  PRINT "JACK ";
510  GOTO 280
520  PRINT "QUEEN ";
530  GOTO 280
540  PRINT "KING ";
550  GOTO 280
560  PRINT "ACE ";
570  GOTO 280
600  PRINT "CLUBS",
610  GOTO 290
620  PRINT "DIAMONDS",
630  GOTO 290
640  PRINT "HEARTS",
650  GOTO 290
660  PRINT "SPADES",
670  GOTO 290
672
700  END
     RUN
NO.4
```

HANDS

| ONE | | TWO | | THREE | | FOUR | |
|-----|-----|-----|-----|-----|-----|-----|-----|
| 3 | CLUBS | DIAMONDS | THREE | SPADES | QUEEN | CLUBS | |
| JACK | CLUBS | 8 | SPADES | 8 | 7 | CLUBS | |
| 7 | SPADES | 8 | SPADES | 5 | 8 | CLUBS | |
| ACE | DIAMONDS | 5 | CLUBS | QUEEN | 8 | DIAMONDS | |
| 2 | DIAMONDS | 5 | HEARTS | ACE | 9 | SPADES | |
| KING | SPADES | 10 | SPADES | JACK | 7 | HEARTS | |
| 10 | HEARTS | 4 | DIAMONDS | SPADES | 2 | HEARTS | |
| JACK | HEARTS | ACE | CLUBS | QUEEN | 3 | SPADES | |
| 4 | CLUBS | KING | SPADES | HEARTS | ACE | SPADES | |
| 8 | DIAMONDS | KING | DIAMONDS | HEARTS | JACK | HEARTS | |
| 9 | HEARTS | 4 | HEARTS | 4 | 6 | DIAMONDS | |
| KING | DIAMONDS | 10 | DIAMONDS | HEARTS | | | |
| 3 | DIAMONDS | 10 | HEARTS | DIAMONDS | | | |

Number 8

```
94   REM * FIND GREATEST COMMON FACTOR
100  PRINT "FIRST #", "SECOND #", "G.C.F."
110  READ A, B
120  IF A = 0 THEN 240
130  PRINT A, B,
140  FOR A = A TO 2 STEP -1
150    IF A/I <> INT(A/I) THEN 170
160    IF B/I = INT(B/I) THEN 200
170  NEXT I
180  PRINT 1
190  GOTO 110
200  PRINT I
210  GOTO 110
212  REM
214  REM
220  DATA 50,35, 28,39
```

## Section 1-4 (cont'd)

### Number 3 (cont'd)

```
660         PRINT "SPACE TAKEN"
670         GOSUB 500
680         GOTO 600
682
684    REM * ENTER NEW MOVE
690    LET A(I,J) = P
700    GOTO 730
710    NEXT J
720
722
724    REM * CHECK FOR WIN
730    FOR I = 1 TO 4
740    LET W(I) = 0
750    NEXT I
752
760    FOR I = 1 TO 3
762
764    REM * CHECK DIAGNALS
770    IF A(I,I) <> P THEN 790
780    LET W(1) = W(1) + 1
790    IF A(I,4-I) <> P THEN 810
800    LET W(2) = W(2) + 1
802
804    REM * CHECK ROWS AND COLUMNS
810    LET W(3) = W(4) = 0
820    FOR J = 1 TO 3
830    IF A(I,J) <> P THEN 850
840    LET W(3) = W(3) + 1
850    IF A(J,I) <> P THEN 870
860    LET W(4) = W(4) + 1
870    NEXT J
872
880    FOR K = 1 TO 4
890    IF W(K) < 3 THEN 930
900    PRINT "YOU WIN #"; Z
910    STOP
920    GOSUB 400
930    NEXT K
940
942    NEXT I
950    RETURN
952
954    REM
        DATA 1,2,3,4,5,6,7,8,9
970    END
RUN
NO.3

THE BOARD
-4    2    3
-4    5    6
-7    8    9

#-1    -2
#-2

-4    -1    6
-7     8    9

-4    5    6
-7    8    9

-2    -1    6
-7     8    9

YOU WIN ?
-2    -1
-7    8    9
```

### Number 6

```
94     REM * COMPAR WITH COMPUTED GOSUB
100    READ A,B
110    IF A = -.01 THEN 320
120    GOSUB SGN(A-B)*2 OF 240,220,200
130    GOTO 100
200    PRINT A; "IS GREATER THAN"; B
210    RETURN
220    PRINT A; "IS EQUAL TO"; B
230    PRINT A; "IS LESS THAN"; B
240    PRINT A; "IS LESS THAN"; B
```

## Chapter 3

### Section 3-2

#### Number 1

```
94     REM * HIGHEST AND LOWEST STRINGS IN DATA
100    READ D$
110    LET H$=D$
120    LET L$=D$
122
130    REM
140    READ D$
150    IF D$="LAST" THEN 220
160    IF L$ <= D$ THEN 190
170    LET L$=D$
180    GOTO 130
190    IF H$ >= D$ THEN 130
200    LET H$=D$
210    GOTO 130
212
220    REM
230    PRINT "LOWEST = ";L$
240    PRINT "HIGHEST = ";H$
242
250    DATA "ONE","TWO","THREE","FOUR","FIVE","LAST"
260    END
NO.1

ONE
TWO
THREE
FOUR
FIVE

LOWEST = FIVE
HIGHEST = TWO
```

#### Number 5

```
100    PRINT
110    READ A$,B$,C$,D$
120    IF A$="STOP" THEN 250
130    IF B$<D$ THEN 190
140    IF B$<C$ THEN 160
150    IF A$<C$ THEN 190
152
160    PRINT D$;", ";C$
170    PRINT B$;", ";A$
180    GOTO 100
182
190    PRINT B$;", ";A$
200    PRINT D$;", ";C$
210    GOTO 100
212
220    DATA "WILLIAM","SMITH","GEORGE","SMITH"
230    DATA "ALICE","JONES","ROBERTA","JONES"
240    DATA "STOP","","",""
250    END
RUN
NO.5

SMITH, GEORGE
SMITH, WILLIAM

JONES, ALICE
JONES, ROBERTA
```

### Section 3-4

#### Number 8

```
94     REM * MULTIPLIES TWO INTEGERS UP TO 20 DIGITS EACH
100    DIM A$(20),B$(20),D$(10),A(20),B(20),C(40)
```

---

```
RUN
NO.11

A$?10
C$?6
6    10

A$?6
C$?10
6    10

A$?A100
C$?A60
A60    A100

A$?A60
C$?A100
A60    A100

A$?STOP
```

## Chapter 3

### Section 3-5

#### Number 1

```
100    DIM A(75)
110    INPUT A$
120    CHANGE A$ TO A
130    LET L = A(0)
140    FOR I = 1 TO L-1
150        FOR J = I+1 TO L
160            IF A(I) <= A(J) THEN 200
170            LET X = A(I)
180            LET A(I) = A(J)
190            LET A(J) = X
200        NEXT J
210    NEXT I
212
220    LET X = 1
230    IF A(X) <> A(X+1) THEN 290
232
234    REM * IF A(X) = A(X+1) THEN MOVE EACH
235    REM   ITEM UP ONE POSITION
240    FOR I = X+1 TO L-1
250        LET A(I) = A(I+1)
260    NEXT I
270    LET L = L-1
280    GOTO 230
282
290    LET X = X+1
300    IF X < L-1 THEN 230
310    LET A(0) = L
312
320    CHANGE A TO A$
330    PRINT A$
340    END
RUN
NO.1
```

? THE QUICK BROWN FOX JUMPED OVER THE LAZY DOGS
ABCDEFGHIJKLMNOPQRSTUVWXYZ

#### Number 2

```
100    DIM N$(100), N(30)
110    READ N
120    MAT READ N$(N)
130    FOR I = 1 TO N
140        PRINT N$(I), TAB(20);
150        CHANGE N$(I) TO N
152
154    REM * SEARCH FOR FIRST SPACE
160        FOR J = N(0) TO 1 STEP -1
170            IF N(J) = 32 THEN 190
180        NEXT J
190        LET N$(I) = EXT$(N$(I),J+1,N(0)) + ", " + EXT$(N$(I),1,J)
```

```
250 RETURN
292 REM
300 DATA 3,4, 1.7,1.1, 31,31, -3,2, 0,0
310 DATA .01,0
380 END
RUN
N0.6

3     IS LESS THAN 4
1.7   IS GREATER THAN 1.1
-31   IS EQUAL TO 31
-3    IS LESS THAN 2
0     IS EQUAL TO 0
```

# Chapter 1

## Section 1-5

### Number 2

```
94  REM * FIND LARGEST RANDOM INTEGER IN ROWS AND COLUMNS
100 DIM A(5,5)
102 REM
104 REM * FILL ARRAY WITH RANDOM INTEGERS
110 FOR I = 1 TO 5
120 FOR J = 1 TO 5
130   LET A(I,J) = INT( RND(-1)*51-25 )
150 NEXT J
160 NEXT I
162 MAT PRINT A;
164 REM * FIND LARGEST INTEGER IN EACH ROW
170 FOR R = 1 TO 5
180 LET C1 = 1
190 LET L = A(R,1)
200 FOR C = 2 TO 5
210   IF A(R,C) <= L THEN 240
220   LET C1 = C
230   LET L = A(R,C)
240 NEXT C
250 PRINT "ROW"; R; "LARGEST IS"; L; "IN COLUMN"; C1
260 NEXT R
270 PRINT
274 REM * FIND LARGEST INTEGER IN EACH COLUMN
280 FOR C = 1 TO 5
290 LET R1 = 1
300 LET L = A(1,C)
310 FOR R = 2 TO 5
320   IF A(R,C) <= L THEN 350
330   LET R1 = R
340   LET L = A(R,C)
350 NEXT R
360 PRINT "COLUMN"; C; "LARGEST IS"; L; "IN ROW"; R1
370 NEXT C
380 END
RUN
N0.2
```

```
-15   -19   -14    3     1
-1    -4    -17   23    17
8     20     6     5   -10
13    -9    23    15   -23
-8     3     8    25    23

ROW 1   LARGEST IS 13   IN COLUMN 4
ROW 2   LARGEST IS 23   IN COLUMN 4
ROW 3   LARGEST IS 20   IN COLUMN 2
ROW 4   LARGEST IS 23   IN COLUMN 3
ROW 5   LARGEST IS 25   IN COLUMN 4

COLUMN 1   LARGEST IS 13   IN ROW 4
COLUMN 2   LARGEST IS 20   IN ROW 3
COLUMN 3   LARGEST IS 23   IN ROW 3
COLUMN 4   LARGEST IS 25   IN ROW 5
COLUMN 5   LARGEST IS 23   IN ROW 5
```

```
110 LET D$="0123456789"
120 READ A$, B$
130 IF A$="STOP" THEN 530
140 PRINT A$;"*";B$;" = ";
142 REM
144 REM * CONVERT A$ TO LIST A
160 LET N=LEN(A$)
164 MAT A=ZER(A)
170 FOR I=1 TO A
180 FOR J=1 TO 10
190   IF A$[I,I]=D$[J,J] THEN 210
200 NEXT J
210 LET A[A+1-I]=J-1
220 NEXT I
222 REM
224 REM * CONVERT B$ TO LIST B
230 LET B=LEN(B$)
240 MAT B=ZER(B)
250 FOR I=1 TO B
260 FOR J=1 TO 10
270   IF B$[I,I]=D$[J,J] THEN 290
280 NEXT J
290 LET B[B+1-I]=J-1
300 NEXT I
302 REM
304 REM * MULTIPLY DIGIT BY DIGIT
310 LET N=A+B
320 MAT C=ZER(N)
340 FOR I=1 TO A
350 LET S=I+J-1
360 LET C[S]=C[S]+A[I]*B[J]
370 IF C[S]<10 THEN 410
380 LET C[S]=C[S]-10
400 GOTO 370
410 NEXT J
420 NEXT I
422 REM
424 REM * PRINT RESULTS
430 FOR C[N]<> 0 THEN 450
440 LET N=N-1
450 FOR I=N TO 1 STEP -1
460 PRINT D$[C[I]+1,C[I]+1];
470 NEXT I
480 PRINT
500 GOTO 120
502 REM
510 DATA "1000","1000","99999999","99999999"
520 DATA "STOP",""
530 END
RUN
N0.8

1000*1000 = 1000000
99999999*99999999 = 9999999800000001
```

### Number 11

```
94  REM * ORDERS NUMERIC CHARACTERS IN STRING VARIABLES
100 DIM A$[25], C$[25]
110 PRINT "A$";
120 INPUT A$
130 IF A$="STOP" THEN 290
160 PRINT "C$";
170 INPUT C$
180 FOR G=1 TO LEN(A$)
200 IF A$[G,G] <> C$[G,G] THEN 210
210 NEXT G
220 IF A$[G,G]="#" THEN 260
230 IF C$[G,G]="#" THEN 260
240 IF LEN(A$)<LEN(C$) THEN 270
250 PRINT C$;" ";A$
260 GOTO 110
270 PRINT A$;" ";C$
280 GOTO 110
290 END
```

```
210 NEXT I
212 REM
220 FOR I = 1 TO N-1
230 FOR J = I+1 TO N
240   IF N$(I) <= N$(J) THEN 280
250   LET N$(I) = N$(J)
260   LET N$(J) = N$(I)
270   LET N$(J) = A$
280 NEXT J
290 NEXT I
300 PRINT
302 PRINT "ORDERED:"
310 PRINT
320 FOR I = 1 TO N
340 PRINT N$(I)
350 NEXT I
352 REM
360 DATA 3
370 DATA GEORGE WASHINGTON, JOHNNY APPLESEED, JOHN G. ADAMS
380 END
RUN
N0.2

GEORGE WASHINGTON    WASHINGTON, GEORGE
JOHNNY APPLESEED     APPLESEED, JOHNNY
JOHN G. ADAMS        ADAMS, JOHN G.

ORDERED:

ADAMS, JOHN G.
APPLESEED, JOHNNY
WASHINGTON, GEORGE
```

### Number 5

```
100 DIM D(10), A(15), B(15), P(30), G(30)
110 LET D$= "0123456789"
120 CHANGE D$ TO D
130 READ A$, B$
140 PRINT A$; " * "; B$
150 CHANGE A$ TO A
152 REM
160 FOR I = 1 TO A(0)
170 FOR J = 1 TO 10
180   IF A(I) <= D(J) THEN 210
190   LET A(I) = J-1
200 GOTO 220
210 NEXT J
220 NEXT I
230 CHANGE B$ TO B
240 FOR J = 1 TO B(0)
250 FOR I = 1 TO 10
260   IF B(J) <> D(J) THEN 290
270   LET B(J) = J-1
280 NEXT J
290 NEXT I
300 MAT P = ZER(A(0)+B(0))
302 REM
310 FOR I = B(0) TO 1 STEP -1
330 FOR J = A(0) TO 1 STEP -I
340 LET K = I+J
350   LET P(K) = P(K) + A(J)*B(I)
360   IF P(K) < 10 THEN 390
370   LET P(K-1) = P(K-1) + INT(P(K)/10)
380   LET P(K) = P(K) - INT(P(K)/10)*10
390 NEXT J
400 NEXT I
402 REM
410 LET P(0) = A(0) + B(0)
420 IF P(1) <> 0 THEN 470
440 FOR I = 1 TO P(0)
450   LET P(I) = P(I+1)
452 NEXT I
460 LET P(0) = P(0) - 1
470 MAT G = ZER(P(0))
480 FOR I = 1 TO P(0)
490   LET G(I) = D(P(I)+1)
500 NEXT I
```

Section 3-5 (cont'd)

Number 5i (cont'd)

```
502   LET Q(C) = P(C)
510   ...
520   CHANGE Q TO Q$
530   PRINT "THE PRODUCT IS "; Q$
532
540   DATA "9999999","9999999"
610   END
RUN
NO.5
```

```
9999999 * 9999999
THE PRODUCT IS 99999980000001
```

Number 8

```
100   DIM A(10), B(10)
110   PRINT "A$";
120   PRINT "A$",
130   INPUT A$
142   IF A$ = "STOP" THEN 320
150   PRINT "B$";
160   INPUT B$
170   CHANGE A$ TO A
180   HANGE B$ TO B
200   IF A(G) > B(G) THEN 260
210   IF A(G) < B(G) THEN 300
```

```
214   REM * ASC(#) = 64 (SEE ASCII CODE)
      IF A(G) > 64 THEN 270
220   IF B(G) > 64 THEN 270
240   IF A(G) < B(G) THEN 300
242
250         GOTO 280
260   NEXT G
270   IF A$ < B$ THEN 300
280   PRINT B$; "  "; A$
290   GOTO 110
300   PRINT A$; "  "; B$
310   GOTO 110
320   END
RUN
NO.8
```

```
A$? 100
B$? 60
60   100
```

```
A$? A60
B$? A100
A60   A100
```

A$? STOP

Chapter 4

Section 4-2

Number 4

```
100   FILES TRY
110   IF END #1 THEN 200
120   LET I=0
130   LET I=I+1
140   READ #1,I
150   IF TYP(-1) <> 3 THEN 130
160   LET I=I+1
170   READ #1,I
180   LET I=I+1
190   GOTO 170
200   PRINT "FILE SIZE IS"; I-1; "RECORDS"
210   END
OPEN-TRY,11
RUN
NO.4
```

```
FIRST EMPTY RECORD IS 1
FILE SIZE IS 11 RECORDS
```

```
12    REM  Y-AXIS.
96    READ S1,S2
100   DEF FNF(X) = (1/S2)*SIN(X)
115   LET K = K/S2
117   LET N = N/S2
130   FOR X = F TO L STEP S1
160   FOR X = F TO (N-K)*S2 STEP S2
410   IF ABS(Y-Y1) < .5*S2 THEN 470
600   DATA  .5,.2
610   DATA  8, 3, -4, 12
620   END
```

RUN
NO.1

x=-4

X = 12

Chapter 5

Section 5-3

Number 6

```
10    REM * THESE CHANGES IN GRAPH3 PROVIDE FOR SCALE
11    REM   FACTORS OF S1 ON THE X-AXIS AND S2 ON THE
12    REM   Y-AXIS.
130   LET T = 5
195   READ S1, S2
215   LET X1 = X*S1
217   LET Y1 = INT(X*S2)
220   LET Y1 = ABS((Y-Y1)*S2-(Y1)^2 - 169 ) > T THEN 300
550   IF ABS((X-L)*S1/10-INT((X-L)*S1/10)) < .05 THEN 590
580   IF ABS((Y-L)*S2/10-INT((Y-L)*S2/10)) < .05 THEN 550
630   DATA  .6, 1
```

RUN
NO.6

```
# OF INCREMENTS?2
AREA IS: 6500.67
```

Chapter 7

Section 7-2

Number 4

```
100   PRINT "TO FIND THE DISTANCE BETWEEN TWO POINTS"
150   PRINT
160   PRINT "POINT A";
170   INPUT X1,Y1
180   PRINT "POINT B";
190   INPUT X2,Y2
200   LET D1 = ( (X2-X1)^2 + (Y2-Y1)^2 )
210   PRINT "DISTANCE AB =";
220   LET D = SQR ( D1 )
230      IF D = INT(D) THEN 320
240   FOR X = INT(D1/2) TO 2 STEP -1
250      IF SQR(X) <> INT(SQR(X)) THEN 270
260         IF D1/X = INT(D1/X) THEN 300
270   NEXT X
272
290   PRINT "SQR("; D1; ")"
300   PRINT SQR(X); "*SQR("; D1/X; ")"
310   GOTO 330
320   PRINT D
330   END
RUN
NO.4
```

```
TO FIND THE DISTANCE BETWEEN TWO POINTS

POINT A? 15,0
POINT B? 0,15
DISTANCE AB = 15 *SQR( 2 )
```

Number 8

```
100   DIM X(20), Y(20)
110   LET N = 0
120   READ A, B
130      IF A = -.001 THEN 180
140   LET N = N+1
150   LET X(N) = A
160   LET Y(N) = B
170   GOTO 120
172
180   FOR P = 1 TO N-1
190      FOR P1 = P+1 TO N
200         PRINT "(";X(P);",";Y(P);")",";
210         PRINT X(P1);",";Y(P1);")";
220            IF X(P) <> X(P1) THEN 280
230            IF Y(P) <> Y(P1) THEN 260
240   PRINT "POINTS COINCIDE"
250   GOTO 340
260   PRINT "EQUATION IS X ="; X(P)
270   GOTO 340
280   LET M = (Y(P1)-Y(P))/(X(P1)-X(P))
290   LET B = Y(P) - M*X(P)
300      IF M <> 0 THEN 330
310   PRINT "EQUATION IS Y ="; B
320   GOTO 340
330   PRINT "EQUATION IS Y ="; M; "*X+"; B ; ")"
340   PRINT
350   NEXT P1
362   NEXT P
495   REM
500   DATA  3,4,  5,6,  -1,6
510   DATA  -1,3,  8,3,  5,6
520   DATA  -.001,0
530   END
RUN
NO.8
```

# Chapter 4

## Section 4-3

### Number 3

```
100 FILES FILE1; FILE2
110 PRINT "FIRST FILE:"
120 READ #1, A
130 PRINT A
140   IF MORE #1 THEN 120
150 PRINT
160 PRINT "SECOND FILE:"
170 READ #2, A
180 PRINT A
190   IF MORE #2 THEN 170
200 PRINT
210 RESTORE #1
220 RESTORE #2
230 PRINT "MERGED LISTS:"
240 READ #1, A
250 READ #2, B
260   IF A <= B THEN 340
270 PRINT B
280   IF MORE #2 THEN 250
290 PRINT A
300 STOP
310 STOP
320 READ #1, A
330 GOTO 290
340 PRINT A
350   IF MORE #1 THEN 410
360 PRINT B
370   IF MORE #2 THEN 390
380 STOP
390 READ #2, B
400 GOTO 360
410 READ #1, A
420 GOTO 260
430 END
RUN
NO.3
```

```
FIRST FILE:
1
2
3
4
5
6
7

SECOND FILE:
1.1
2.2
3.3
4.4
5.5

MERGED LISTS:
1
1.1
2
2.2
3
3.3
4
4.4
5
5.5
6
7
```

# Chapter 5

## Section 5-2

### Number 1

```
10 REM * THESE CHANGES IN GRAPH2 PROVIDE FOR SCALE
11 REM   FACTORS OF S1 ON THE X-AXIS AND S2 ON THE
```

# Chapter 6

### Number 6

```
94  REM * SIMPSON'S RULE
100 DEF FNS(X) = 2*X+3 - 2*X+2 + X + 5
110 READ F,T
120 PRINT "# OF INCREMENTS:";
130 INPUT I
140 LET W = (T-F)/I
150 LET A1 = FNS(F)
160 FOR C = 1 TO I-1
170   LET X = F + C*W
180   IF C/2 = INT(C/2) THEN 210
190   LET A1 = A1 + 4*FNS(X)
200   GOTO 220
210   LET A1 = A1 + 2*FNS(X)
220 NEXT C
230 LET A1 = A1 + FNS(T)
240 LET A = A1*(W/3)
250 PRINT "AREA IS:"; A
252
254 REM
260 DATA  -3,11
270 END
```

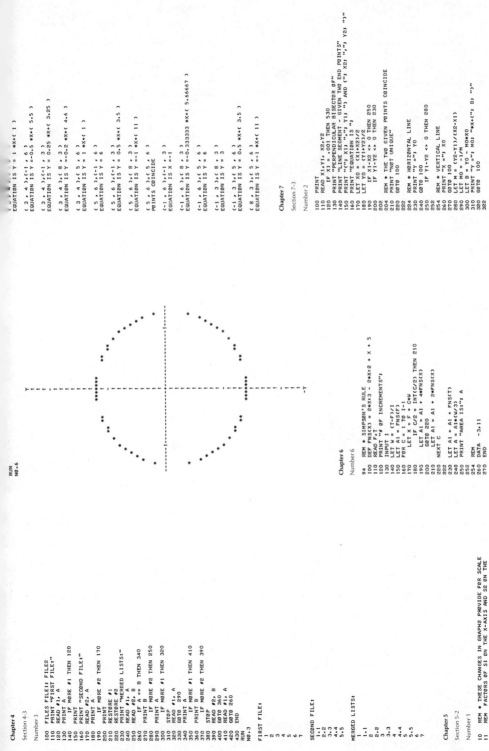

```
EQUATION IS Y = 1 *X+( 1 )

( 3 , 4 )<(-1 , 6 )
EQUATION IS Y =-0.5 *X+( 5.5 )

( 3 , 4 )<(-1 , 3 )
EQUATION IS Y = 0.25 *X+( 3.25 )

( 3 , 4 )<( 8 , 3 )
EQUATION IS Y =-0.2 *X+( 4.6 )

( 3 , 4 )<( 5 , 6 )
EQUATION IS Y = 1 *X+( 1 )

( 5 , 6 )<(-1 , 6 )
EQUATION IS Y = 6

( 5 , 6 )<(-1 , 3 )
EQUATION IS Y = 0.5 *X+( 3.5 )

( 5 , 6 )<( 8 , 3 )
EQUATION IS Y =-1 *X+( 11 )

( 5 , 6 )<( 5 , 6 )
POINTS COINCIDE

(-1 , 6 )<(-1 , 3 )
EQUATION IS X =-1

(-1 , 6 )<( 8 , 3 )
EQUATION IS Y =-0.333333 *X+( 5.66667 )

(-1 , 6 )<( 5 , 6 )
EQUATION IS Y = 6

(-1 , 3 )<( 8 , 3 )
EQUATION IS Y = 3

(-1 , 3 )<( 5 , 6 )
EQUATION IS Y = 0.5 *X+( 3.5 )

( 8 , 3 )<( 5 , 6 )
EQUATION IS Y =-1 *X+( 11 )
```

# Chapter 7

## Section 7-3

### Number 2

```
100 PRINT
110 READ X1,Y1, X2,Y2
120   IF X1 =.001 THEN 530
130 PRINT "PERPENDICULAR BISECTOR OF"
140 PRINT "LINE SEGMENT - GIVEN TWO END POINTS"
150 PRINT "(";X1;",";Y1;") AND (";X2;",";Y2;")"
160 PRINT "EQUATION IS ";
170 LET X0 = (X1+X2)/2
180 LET Y0 = (Y1+Y2)/2
190   IF X1-X2 <> 0 THEN 250
200   IF Y1-Y2 <> 0 THEN 230
202 REM * THE TWO GIVEN POINTS COINCIDE
204 PRINT "NOT UNIQUE"
220 GOTO 100
222
224 REM * HORIZONTAL LINE
230 PRINT "Y =";Y0
240 GOTO 100
250   IF Y1-Y2 <> 0 THEN 280
252
254 REM * VERTICAL LINE
260 PRINT "X =";X0
270 GOTO 100
280 LET M = (Y2-Y1)/(X2-X1)
290 LET MO = -1/M
300 LET B = YO - MO*XO
310 PRINT "Y =";MO;"*X+(";B;")"
320 GOTO 100
322
```

## Section 7-3 (cont'd)

### Number 2 (cont'd)

```
494  REM
500  DATA  1,2, 4,7,    4,7, 4,3
510  DATA  -3,9, 4,5,   4,-7, 4,-7
520  DATA  .001,0,0,0
530  END
RUN
NO.2
```

```
PERPENDICULAR BISECTOR OF
LINE SEGMENT - GIVEN TWO END POINTS
( 1 , 2 ) AND ( 4 , 7 )
EQUATION IS Y =-0.6 *X+( 6 )

PERPENDICULAR BISECTOR OF
LINE SEGMENT - GIVEN TWO END POINTS
( 4 , 7 ) AND ( 4 , 3 )
EQUATION IS Y = 5

PERPENDICULAR BISECTOR OF
LINE SEGMENT - GIVEN TWO END POINTS
( 4 , 5 ) AND ( 4 , 7 )
EQUATION IS Y = 1.75 *X+( 6 +.125 )

PERPENDICULAR BISECTOR OF
LINE SEGMENT - GIVEN TWO END POINTS
( 4 , -7 ) AND ( 4 , -7 )
EQUATION IS NOT UNIQUE
```

### Number 4

```
100   PRINT
110   GOSUB 5000
120   LET K1 = K
130   IF K <> 3 THEN 150
140   LET M2 = M
150   GOSUB 5000(15)) "AND"
500   ON K GOTO 600, 700, 800, 1300
502
600   ON K1 GOTO 1100, 1000, 1200, 1300
700   ON K1 GOTO 1000, 1100, 1200, 1300
800   ON K1 GOTO 1200, 1200, 1400, 1300
900
1000  PRINT "PERPENDICULAR"
1010  GOTO 100
1100  PRINT "PARALLEL"
1110  GOTO 100
1200  PRINT "NEITHER"
1210  PRINT "MEANINGLESS"
1300  GOTO 100
1310      IF M*M2 = -1 THEN 1000
1400      IF M = M2 THEN 1100
1410  GOTO 1200
1422
5000  READ A, B, C
5010      IF A = -.001 THEN 9999
5020  PRINT A; "*X+("; B; ")*Y+("; C1 ")=0     ";
5030      IF A = 0 THEN 5100
5040      IF B = 0 THEN 5200
5050  LET M = -A/B
5060  LET K = 3
5070  PRINT "SLOPE ="; M
5080  RETURN
5100      IF B = 0 THEN 5300
5110  LET K = 1
5120  PRINT "HORIZONTAL"
5130  LET K = 2
5140  RETURN
5200  LET K = 4
5210  PRINT "VERTICAL"
5220  RETURN
5300  PRINT "MEANINGLESS"
5310  LET K = 4
5320  RETURN
5322
6000  DATA  1,1,1, 2,2,4,   0,1,2, 1,0,2
```

## Chapter 7

### Section 7-5

### Number 4

```
422  REM
424  REM * THE FOLLOWING NEW LINES IN PROGRAM
425  REM PYTH3 WILL PRODUCE THE DESIRED RESULTS
430  FOR P = 1 TO 3
435      IF D(P)↑2 > D(P+1)↑2+D(P+2)↑2 THEN 475
440  NEXT P
442
445  LET D = D(1)
450  FOR P = 2 TO 3
455      IF ABS(D-D(P)) > .000001 THEN 485
462
465  PRINT "EQUILATERAL AND EQUIANGULAR"
470  GOTO 110
475  PRINT "OBTUSE TRIANGLE WITH LONG SIDE DETERMINED BY"
480  GOTO 510
485  PRINT "ACUTE TRIANGLE"
490  GOTO 110
492
494  REM
810  DATA  3,  0,0,   2,0,   1,1.73205
820  DATA  1,  1,2,   5,-1,  6,15
830  DATA  1,  0,0,   0,3,   4,0
840  DATA  0   -2,6,  1,2,   9,8
RUN
NO.4
```

```
( 0 , 0 ), ( 2 , 0 ) AND ( 1 , 1.73205 )
EQUILATERAL AND EQUIANGULAR

( 1 , 2 ), ( 5 , -1 ) AND ( 6 , 15 )
OBTUSE TRIANGLE WITH LONG SIDE DETERMINED BY
POINTS( 5 , -1 ) AND ( 6 , 15 )

( 0 , 0 ), ( 0 , 3 ) AND ( 4 , 0 )
RIGHT TRIANGLE WITH HYPOTENUSE DETERMINED BY
POINTS( 0 , 3 ) AND ( 4 , 0 )

( -2 , 6 ), ( 1 , 2 ) AND ( 9 , 8 )
RIGHT TRIANGLE WITH HYPOTENUSE DETERMINED BY
POINTS( 1 , 2 ) AND ( 9 , 8 )
```

### Number 5

```
100  FOR A = 3 TO 98
110  FOR B = A+1 TO 99
120  LET K1 = SQR(A↑2 + B↑2)
130      IF K1 <> INT(K1) THEN 160
140      IF K1 > 100 THEN 170
150  PRINT A; B; K1
160  NEXT B
170  NEXT A
180  END
RUN
NO.5
```

```
3    4    5
5    12   13
6    8    10
8    15   17
9    12   15
9    40   41
10   24   26
12   16   20
13   84   85
14   48   50
15   20   25
15   36   39
16   30   34
18   24   30
```

## Chapter 8

### Section 8-1

### Number 2

```
100  DIM P(20), F(10), S(10)
110  FOR W = 1 TO 10
120  LET F(W) = S(W)   :   P(W*10) = P(W*10) = 0
130
132
134  REM * READ AND PRINT COEFFICIENTS
140  READ A
150      IF A = 0 THEN 420
160  FOR X = 1 TO 1 STEP -1
170  READ F(X)
180  PRINT F(X);
190  NEXT X
200  PRINT
210  READ B
220  FOR Y = B TO 1 STEP -1
230  READ S(Y)
240  PRINT S(Y);
250  NEXT Y
260  PRINT
262
270  REM * FIND AND PRINT PRODUCT
280  PRINT "PRODUCT =";
290  FOR I = 1 TO A
300  FOR J = 1 TO B
         LET P(I+J-1) = P(I+J-1) + F(I)*S(J)
310  NEXT J
320  NEXT I
330  FOR Z = A+B-1 TO 1 STEP -1
         PRINT P(Z);
340  NEXT Z
350  PRINT
360  PRINT
370  PRINT
380  GOTO 110
382
384  REM
390  DATA  5,  3,2,0,2,1,  3,  2,5,2
400  DATA  2,  3,2,        2,  2,3
410  DATA  0
420  END
RUN
NO.2
```

```
3  2  0  2  1
2  5  2
PRODUCT =  6   19   16   8   12   9   2

3  2
2  3
PRODUCT =  6   13   6
```

## Chapter 9

### Section 9-1

### Number 1

```
100  DIM F(50)
102
104  REM * STORE FIBONACCI NUMBERS IN A LIST
110  LET F(1) = 1
120  LET F(2) = 1
130  FOR X = 3 TO 18
         LET F(X) = F(X-1) + F(X-2)
140  NEXT X
142
144  REM * NOW PRINT RESULTS
150  PRINT "F(X)↑2", "F(X-1)*F(X+1)", "DIFFERENCE"
160  FOR X = 2 TO 17
170      LET A = F(X)↑2
180      LET B = F(X-1)*F(X+1)
200      PRINT X, A, B, A-B
202  NEXT X
210  END
RUN
```

```
6010  DATA  1,2,3,  2,-1,-3,  3,4,5,  8,9,2
6020  DATA  0,0,1,  2,3,4
6030  DATA  -.001,0,0
9999  END
RUN
NO.4
```

```
1 *X*( 1 )+Y*( )+0      SLOPE =-1
                 AND
2 *X*( 2 )+Y*( 4 )+0    SLOPE =-1
PARALLEL

0 *X*( 1 )+Y*( 2 )+0    HORIZONTAL
                 AND
1 *X*( 0 )+Y*( )+0      VERTICAL
PERPENDICULAR

1 *X*( 2 )+Y*( 3 )+0    SLOPE =-0.5
                 AND
2 *X*( -1 )+Y*( -3 )+0  SLOPE = 2
PERPENDICULAR

3 *X*( 4 )+Y*( 5 )+0    SLOPE =-0.75
                 AND
8 *X*( 9 )+Y*( 2 )+0    SLOPE =-0.888889
NEITHER

0 *X*( 0 )+Y*( 1 )+0    MEANINGLESS
                 AND
2 *X*( 3 )+Y*( 4 )+0    SLOPE =-0.666667
MEANINGLESS
```

```
20   21   29
20   48   52
21   28   35
21   72   75
24   32   40
24   70   51
24   60   74
25   36   65
27   45   53
28   45   100
28   40   50
30   72   78
30   40   68
32   60   50
33   44   65
33   56   91
36   48   60
36   84   85
36   77   77
39   52   89
39   80   80
40   42   58
40   75   85
42   56   70
45   60   55
48   55   73
48   64   80
51   68   85
54   72   90
57   76   95
60   63   87
60   80   100
65   72   97
```

```
              2
1             3
4             10
9             24
25            40
64            65
169           168
441           442
1156          1155
3025          3026
7921          7920
20737         20736
54289.        54288.
142130.       142129.
372100.       372099.
              94170.
2.550041E+06  2.550041E+06
```

## Number 2

```
100  DIM F(25), L(20)
110  LET F(1) = F(2) = 1
120  FOR X = 3 TO 25
130      LET F(X) = F(X-1) + F(X-2)
140  NEXT X
142
150  FOR X = 2 TO 24
160      FOR Y = X+1 TO 25
162
164  REM * USE THE EUCLIDEAN ALGORITHM TO
165  REM     FIND THE GCF
170      LET N = F(X)
180      LET D = F(Y)
190      LET I = INT(N/D)
200      LET R = N - I*D
210      IF R = 0 THEN 250
220          LET N = D
230          LET D = R
240          GOTO 190
242
244  REM * ADD THE LATEST GCF TO THE L LIST
245  REM     IF IT IS NOT ALREADY THERE.
250      FOR Z = 1 TO N1
260          IF L(Z) = D THEN 300
270      NEXT Z
280      LET N1 = N1 + 1
290      LET L(N1) = D
300  NEXT Y
310  NEXT X
314  REM * NOW PRINT ALL DIFFERENT GCF'S.
320  FOR X = 1 TO N1
330      PRINT L(X)
340  NEXT X
350  END
RUN
NO.2

 1   2   3   5   8   13   21   34   55   89   144
```

## Number 3

```
100  DIM F(50)
110  LET F(1) = F(2) = 1
120  FOR X = 3 TO 30
130      LET F(X) = F(X-1) + F(X-2)
140  NEXT X
142
150  FOR X = 2 TO 20
160      PRINT F(X)/F(X-1),
172
180  END
RUN
NO.3

 1            1.5        1.6
 .625         1.61905    1.61818
 1.61538      1.61806    1.61765    1.66667    1.61804
 1.61798      1.61803    1.61803    1.61803    1.61803
 1.61803      1.61803    1.61803    1.61803    1.61803
```

# Chapter 7

## Section 7-4

### Number 1

```
100  PRINT
110  READ M1, B1
120      IF M1 = -.001 THEN 260
130  PRINT "LINE 1 Y = ("; M1; ")*X+("; B1; ")"
140  READ M2, B2
150  PRINT "LINE 2 Y = ("; M2; ")*X+("; B2; ")"
160      IF M1 <> M2 THEN 190
170  PRINT "THE LINES ARE PARALLEL"
180  GOTO 100
190  LET X = (B2-B1)/(M1-M2)
200  LET Y = M1*X+B1
210  PRINT "INTERSECT AT ("; X1; ","; Y1; ")"
220  GOTO 100
222
224  REM
230  DATA  3,-7, -4,14,  1,2, 3,4
240  DATA  5,3, 5,8,  2,-1, 5,-11
250  DATA  -.001,0
260  END
RUN
NO.1

LINE 1 Y = ( 3 )*X+(-7 )
LINE 2 Y = (-4 )*X+( 14 )
INTERSECT AT ( 3  , 2 )

LINE 1 Y = ( 1 )*X+( 2 )
LINE 2 Y = ( 3 )*X+( 4 )
INTERSECT AT (-1  , 1 )

LINE 1 Y = ( 5 )*X+( 3 )
LINE 2 Y = ( 5 )*X+( 8 )
THE LINES ARE PARALLEL

LINE 1 Y = ( 5 )*X+(-11 )
LINE 2 Y = ( 5 )*X+(-11 )
INTERSECT AT ( 0  , -11 )
```

### Number 7

```
94   REM * DOES NOT HANDLE PAIRS OF POINTS
95   REM    ON A VERTICAL LINE
100  DIM X(20), Y(20)
110  PRINT
120  READ T
130      IF T = 0 THEN 530
140  LET N = 0
150  READ X1, Y1
160      IF X1 = -.001 THEN 220
170  LET N = N+1
180  LET X(N) = X1
190  LET Y(N) = Y1
200  PRINT "("; X1; ","; Y1; ")"
210  GOTO 150
220  FOR I = 2 TO N-1
230      LET M2 = (Y(I+1)-Y(I)) / (X(I+1)-X(I))
240      IF M1 <> M2 THEN 300
250      LET M1 = M2
260  NEXT I
272
280  PRINT N; "POINTS COLLINEAR"
290  GOTO 110
300  PRINT "POINTS NON-COLLINEAR"
310  GOTO 110
380
494  REM
500  DATA  999, 1,2, 3,4, 5,6, 7,8, 9,10, -.001,0
510  DATA  999, 1,8, 3,9, 2,7, 3,2, -.001,0
520  DATA  0
530  END
RUN
NO.7

( 1 , 2 )
( 3 , 4 )
( 5 , 6 )
( 7 , 8 )
( 9 , 10 )
5 POINTS COLLINEAR

( 1 , 8 )
( 3 , 9 )
( 2 , 7 )
( 3 , 2 )
POINTS NON-COLLINEAR
```

Section 9-1 (cont'd)

Number 4

```
100  DIM F(50)
110  LET F(1) = 1
120  LET F(2) = 3
130  FØR I = 3 TØ 20
140     LET F(I) = F(I-1) + F(I-2)
150  NEXT I
152
160  FØR I = 1 TØ 20
170     PRINT F(I),
180  NEXT I
182
190  END
RUN
NØ.4

 1              3              4              7              11
 18             29             47             76             123
 199            322            521            843            1364
 2207           3571           5778           9349           15127
```

Number 9

```
100  LET D = 10
110  LET B = 0
120  LET D = 3*D/4
130  LET B = B+1
140     IF D > 1/12 THEN 120
150  LET D = INT( D*1000 )/1000
160  PRINT B; "BØUNCES"; D; "HEIGHT"
170  END
RUN
NØ.9

 17 BØUNCES 0.075 HEIGHT
```

Number 10

```
100  LET A = 2↑63
110  PRINT A; "GRAINS"
120     IF A > 1000 THEN 150
130  PRINT "YES THEY WILL FIT"
140  STØP
150  PRINT "NØ THEY WILL NEVER FIT IN THAT LITTLE SPACE"
160  END
RUN
NØ.10

 9.22337E+18 GRAINS
NØ THEY WILL NEVER FIT IN THAT LITTLE SPACE
```

**Chapter 9**

Section 9-2

Number 2

```
100  PRINT "N", "1+(2/3)↑N", "(1+(2/3))↑N"
110  FØR N = 1 TØ 10
120     GØSUB 180
130  NEXT N
132
140  FØR N = 20 TØ 70 STEP 10
150     GØSUB 180
160  NEXT N
162
170  STØP
172
180  PRINT N, 1+(2/3)↑N, (1+(2/3))↑N
190  RETURN
200  END
RUN
NØ.2

N               1+(2/3)↑N       (1+(2/3))↑N
 1               1.66667         1.66667
 2               1.44444         2.77778
 3               1.2963          4.62963
 4               1.19753         7.71605
```

```
110  FØR I = 1 TØ 12
120     LET S = S+I
130     LET S1 = S1+S
140  NEXT I
142
150  PRINT S1; "GIFTS ALL TØGETHER"
160  END
RUN
NØ.3

 364  GIFTS ALL TØGETHER
```

**Chapter 9**

Section 9-4

Number 4

```
100  PRINT "HØW MANY PØINTS";
110  INPUT N1
120  LET C = 0
130  RANDØMIZE
140  FØR N = 1 TØ N1
150     LET X = RND
160     LET Y = RND
170        IF X↑2 + Y↑2 >= 1 THEN 190
180     LET C = C+1
190  NEXT N
192
200  PRINT C; "IN THE CIRCLE"; 4*C/N1
210  END
RUN
NØ.4

HØW MANY PØINTS? 2500
 1968  IN THE CIRCLE 3.1488


RUN
NØ.4

HØW MANY PØINTS? 2500
 1958  IN THE CIRCLE 3.1328
```

**Chapter 10**

Section 10-1

Number 1

```
100  DIM S(3,4),P(4,1),M(3,1),T(1,4),A(1,1)
110  MAT READ S, P
120  FØR R = 1 TØ 3
130     FØR C = 1 TØ 4
140        LET T(1,C) = T(1,C) + S(R,C)
150     NEXT C
160  NEXT R
162
170  MAT A = T*P
180  MAT PRINT A
182
184  REM
190  DATA  30,800,50,20,   50,31,40,10,   0,500,50,90
200  DATA  1,.39,.49,3.79
210  END
RUN
NØ.1

 1122.49
```

Number 4

```
100  DIM A(3,1), B(4,3), C(4,1), N$(4)
110  MAT READ A, B, N$
120  MAT C = B*A
122
130  FØR I = 1 TØ 4
140     PRINT C(I,1); TAB(10); N$(I)
150  NEXT I
```

```
INV(A)

 0.38587         -2.17391E-2      0.173913
 7.06522E-2       0.108696        0.130435
-6.52174E-2       0.130435       -4.34783E-2

A*INV(A)

 1                0              -3.72529E-9
 7.45058E-9       1.              9.31323E-10
 7.45058E-9      -3.72529E-9      1

INV(A)*A

 1               -9.31323E-9      5.58794E-9
 3.72529E-9       1.             -9.31323E-9
 9.31323E-10     -2.79397E-9      1.
```

Number 4

```
100  DIM C(3,3), K(3,1), S(3,1), I(3,3)
110  MAT READ C, K
120  MAT I = INV(C)
130  MAT S = I*K
140  MAT PRINT S
142
145  REM
150  DATA  2,-9,-5,   7,-6,5,    9,-6,5
160  DATA  2,-35,-39
170  END
RUN
NØ.4

-2
 1.
-3.
```

Number 10

```
100  DIM A(3,3), B(3,3), C(3,3), D(3,3), E(3,3)
110  MAT READ A, B
120  MAT C = A*B
130  MAT D = INV(C)
140  PRINT
150  PRINT "INV(A*B)"
160  MAT PRINT D
170  MAT C = INV(A)
180  MAT D = INV(B)
190  MAT E = D*C
200  PRINT
210  PRINT "INV(B)*INV(A)"
220  MAT PRINT E
222
224  REM
230  DATA  1,-2,3,   5,-1,-2,   0,3,4
240  DATA  2,-4,0,   -3,1,2,    5,2,-5
250  END
RUN
NØ.10


INV(A*B)

 1.50575         -1.20115        -2.72989
 0.747126        -0.649425       -1.38506
 1.77012         -1.45402        -3.3046

INV(B)*INV(A)

 1.50575         -1.20115        -2.72989
 0.747127        -0.649425       -1.38506
 1.77012         -1.45402        -3.3046
```

Number 11

```
100  DIM C(10,10), K(10,1), I(10,10), S(10,1)
```

```
5        1.13169       12.8601
6        1.08779       21.4335
7        1.03853       35.7225
8        1.03902       59.5374
9        1.02601       99.2291
10       1.01734       165.382
20       1.0003        27351.1
30       1.00001       4.5233E+06
40       1             7.4809E+08
50       1             1.2370E+11
60       1             2.0461E+13
70       1             3.3838E+15
```

**Number 5**

```
100   DIM F(20)
110   LET F(1) = F(2) = 1
120   FOR N = 3 TO 20
130     LET F(N) = F(N-1) + F(N-2)
140   NEXT N
142
150   PRINT "BY ADDITION","BY FORMULA"
160   LET SO = SQR(5)
170   FOR N = 1 TO 20
180     LET S1 = ((1+SO)*N-(1-SO)*N)/((2*N)*SO)
190     PRINT F(N), S1
200   NEXT N
210   END
NO.5
```

```
BY ADDITION    BY FORMULA
1              1
1              1
2              2
3              3
5              5
8              8
13             13.
21             21.
34             34.
55             55.
89             89.
144            144.
233            233.
377            377.
610            610.
987            987.
1597           1597.
2584           2584.
4181           4181.
6765           6765.
```

**Chapter 9**

Section 9-3

Number 3

```
94  REM * THE TWELVE DAYS OF CHRISTMAS
100 LET S = S1 = 0
```

```
152  REM
154  DATA  800, 200, 1500
170  DATA  3,1,4,  1,1,2,  9,2,3,  15,8,12
180  DATA  BULBS, SWITCHES, METERS OF WIRE, SCREWS
190  DATA  END
RUN
NO.4
```

```
8600      BULBS
4000      SWITCHES
12100     METERS OF WIRE
31600     SCREWS
```

**Number 6**

```
100  DIM A(1,3),B(3,4),C(4,1),D(1,4),E(1,1)
110  MAT READ A, B, C
120  MAT D = A*B
130  MAT E = D*C
140  MAT PRINT E
142
145  REM
150  DATA  1,1,1
160  DATA  30,800,50,20,  50,31,40,10,  0,500,50,90
170  DATA  1,.39,.49,3.79
180  END
RUN
NO.6
```

```
1122.49
```

**Chapter 10**

Section 10-2

Number 1

```
100  DIM A(3,3), B(3,3), C(3,3)
110  MAT READ A
120  MAT B = INV(A)
130  PRINT "INV(A)"
140  MAT PRINT B
150  MAT C = A*B
160  PRINT
170  PRINT "A*INV(A)"
180  MAT PRINT C
190  MAT C = B*A
200  PRINT
210  PRINT "INV(A)*A"
220  MAT PRINT C
222
224  REM
230  DATA  4,-4,4,  1,1,7,  -3,9,-8
240  END
RUN
NO.1
```

```
130  MAT READ C(N,N), K(N,1)
140  PRINT "COEFFICIENT MATRIX"
150  MAT PRINT C
160  PRINT
170  PRINT "CONSTANT TERMS"
180  MAT PRINT K
190  MAT I = INV(C)
200  MAT S = I*K
210  PRINT
220  PRINT "SOLUTIONS"
230  MAT PRINT S
240  PRINT
250  GOTO 110
252
254  REM
260  DATA  2,  3,1,  5,-3
270  DATA  7,21
280  DATA  3,  2,3,-1,  3,0,1,  1,-2,-5
290  DATA  20,0,6
300  DATA  0
310  END
RUN
NO.11
```

```
COEFFICIENT MATRIX

3      1
5      -3

CONSTANT TERMS

7
21

SOLUTIONS

3.
-2.

COEFFICIENT MATRIX

2      3      -1
3      0      -5
1      -2

CONSTANT TERMS

20
0
6

SOLUTIONS

1.
5.
-3.
```

# INDEX